GCSE OCR 21st Century
Core Science
The Workbook

This book is for anyone doing **GCSE OCR 21st Century Core Science** at foundation level.

It's full of **tricky questions**... each one designed to make you **sweat** — because that's the only way you'll get any **better**.

There are questions to see **what facts** you know. There are questions to see how well you can **apply those facts**. And there are questions to see what you know about **how science works**.

It's also got some daft bits in to try and make the whole experience at least vaguely entertaining for you.

What CGP is all about

Our sole aim here at CGP is to produce the highest quality books — carefully written, immaculately presented and dangerously close to being funny.

Then we work our socks off to get them out to you — at the cheapest possible prices.

Contents

Published by Coordination Group Publications Ltd.

Editors:
Amy Boutal, Ellen Bowness, Tom Cain, Katherine Craig, Sarah Hilton, Kate Houghton, Rose Parkin, Ami Snelling, Laurence Stamford, Julie Wakeling, Sarah Williams.

Contributors:
Michael Aicken, Mike Bossart, Jane Davies, Mark A Edwards, Adrian Schmit, Paul Warren.

ISBN: 978 1 84146 626 2

With thanks to Barrie Crowther, Ian Francis and Sue Hocking for the proofreading.

With thanks to Jan Greenway for the copyright research.

Photographs on page 3 reproduced with kind permission from Adrian Schmit.

Graph on page 17 reproduced with kind permission from Earth System Research Laboratory, National Oceanic and Atmospheric Administration, and Scripps Institution of Oceanography, University of California.

Data on page 22 courtesy of Haynes Publishing.

Article on page 23 based on information from, "Nino Künzli, Michael Jerrett, Wendy J. Mack, Bernardo Beckerman, Laurie LaBree, Frank Gilliland, Duncan Thomas, John Peters, and Howard N. Hodis. Ambient Air Pollution and Atherosclerosis in Los Angeles. Environmental Health Perspectives 113:201–206 (2005)" with kind permission from the publisher.

Data on page 36 courtesy of NASA/JPL-Caltech.

Data on page 46 reproduced with kind permission from the Health Protection Agency, www. HPA.org.uk.

Data on page 54 reproduced with kind permission from the British Heart Foundation © 2006.

Data on page 76 © Crown Copyright 2006, data supplied by the Met Office.

Timeline on page 101 reproduced with permission from New Scientist.

Data on page 109 courtesy of NPL, http://www.npl.co.uk © Crown Copyright 2006.

Groovy website: www.cgpbooks.co.uk

Printed by Elanders Hindson Ltd, Newcastle upon Tyne.
Jolly bits of clipart from CorelDRAW®

Based on the classic CGP style created by Richard Parsons.

Genes, Chromosomes and DNA

Q1 Tick the boxes to show whether the following statements are **true** or **false**.

True False

a) The nucleus of a cell contains instructions for how an organism develops.

b) Genes are short lengths of chromosomes.

c) Genes are found on chromosomes.

d) There are 23 pairs of genes.

e) Genes are instructions for a cell that describe how to make proteins.

Q2 Some **structures** found in the human body are named below. Put them in the table in order of **size**, from **smallest** to **largest**. The first one has been done for you.

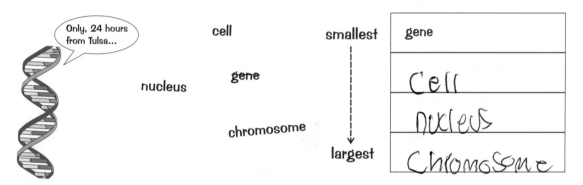

Only, 24 hours from Tulsa...

cell

nucleus

gene

chromosome

smallest

largest

gene
Cell
nucleus
Chromosome

Q3 Join **names** of the genetic structures to their **descriptions**. One has been done already.

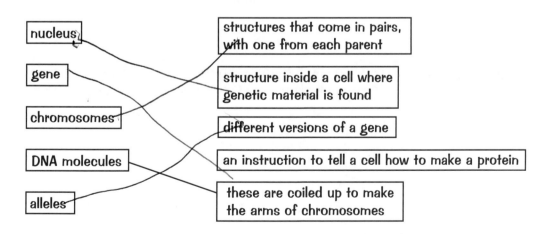

nucleus

gene

chromosomes

DNA molecules

alleles

structures that come in pairs, with one from each parent

structure inside a cell where genetic material is found

different versions of a gene

an instruction to tell a cell how to make a protein

these are coiled up to make the arms of chromosomes

Top Tips: Remember humans have 23 pairs of chromosomes, that's 46 in total. Chromosomes carry genes that provide instructions for cells about how to make different proteins. It's the different proteins that are responsible for all of your characteristics like hair colour and eye colour.

Inheritance

Q1   Complete the passage using the words below.

| different   pairs   resemble   alleles   exactly   23 |

During fertilisation the ......23........... chromosomes in the sperm

combine with the ....allels............ chromosomes in the egg to form 23

......different........ of chromosomes. Each chromosome in a pair has come

from a ....different.......... parent. This means there may be different

versions of the genes — called ......allels.......... . Because children get

their alleles from both parents they tend to ....resemble...... both parents

but never look ...exactley......... the same as either one.

Q2   An organism's genes are carried in **chromosomes**.

a)   How many chromosomes would you find in a human **skin** cell? Circle the correct answer.

    13   83   46   (46)   16   (27)   91

b)   i)   How many chromosomes would you find in a human **sex** cell? Circle the correct answer.

    13   83   46   (23)   16   27   91

ii)   How many **copies** of each chromosome would you find in a **sex** cell.

....

Q3   The diagram shows a **pair** of human **chromosomes**. These chromosomes carry a **gene** for **ear lobes**. The position of the gene is marked on one of the chromosomes in the diagram.

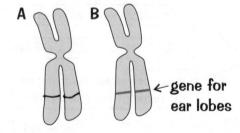

A   B

← gene for
ear lobes

a)   Draw the position of the gene for ear lobes on chromosome A.

b)   If chromosome A came from the **mother** where must chromosome B come from?

......the......dad...

Inheritance

Q4 Complete the following passage using the words below.

XX	sex	XY	sperm	Y	egg	X

The 23rd pair of chromosomes in humans decide whether you are male or female. They are called the ......Y........ chromosomes. There are two types, the ......Y........ chromosome, which can be found in eggs or sperm, and the ......sex........ chromosome, which is found in ....sperm........ cells but never in ......egg........ cells. Somebody with the chromosomes ....XX........ would be male, where as someone with the chromosomes ....XY........ would be female.

My son Jeremy shall inherit my stamp collection and my chromosomes.

Q5 The picture below shows two **brothers**. They have the **same parents** but don't bear a close resemblance to one another.

Complete the following statements by circling the correct word(s) to explain why two brothers (or sisters) can look quite different from each other, even though they have the same parents.

Despite inheriting **half** / **all** / **none** of their genes from the same mother and **all** / **none** / **half** from the same father, siblings don't look identical. This is because of the way **sex cells** / **liver cells** are made and the way they **combine** / **separate**. There are **tens** / **millions** of different combinations. Every person in the world will have **a unique** / **the same** combination of alleles — that's why no two people in the world are exactly the same, with the exception of **cousins** / **identical twins**.

Top Tips: Remember the chromosomes in a pair carry the same genes in the same places. But because each of the chromosomes in a pair come from a different parent you may well have different versions of these genes — these are called alleles.

Module B1 — You and Your Genes

Variation

Q1 Tick the boxes to show whether the following are **true** or **false**.

True   False

a) The two chromosomes in a pair are identical.

b) Only one chromosome from each pair enters a sperm or egg cell.

c) All the egg cells a woman produces are genetically identical.

d) Fertilisation occurs when sperm cells are formed.

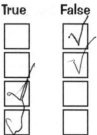

Q2 The diagram below shows the nuclei of two organisms that contain only **four pairs** of chromosomes. Different **alleles** are shown using different shades of the same colour.

Organism 1   **Organism 2**

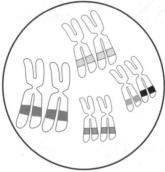   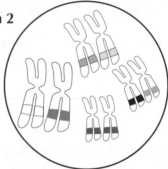

Look carefully at the different coloured chromosomes, remember one in each pair must come from each parent.

Organisms 1 and 2 **mate**. Put a tick in the correct boxes to show the nuclei of the cells that could be produced at fertilisation.

A   B   C   D

Q3 The table lists some **variations** seen in human beings. Indicate if the variation is caused by **genetic** factors, **environmental** factors, or **both**.

Variation	Genetic	Environmental	Both
Height			
Eye colour			
Hairstyle			
Skin colour			
Blood group			

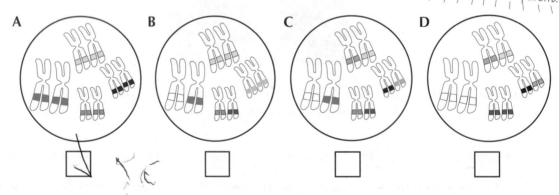

Module B1 — You and Your Genes

Variation

Q4 Some diseases can be caused by both a person's **genes** and their **environment**. Read the statements about two families, the Greens and the Perkins and answer the questions that follow.

- The Greens and the Perkins live next door to each other.
- For generations, the men in both families have worked in the local paint factory.
- Mr Green has been diagnosed with cancer. His father, who also worked in the factory, died of the same cancer some years ago.
- Mr Perkins and his father are both healthy.
- Mr Green has two brothers who have moved away from the area and have different jobs. Neither man has developed cancer.

a) What evidence is there that Mr Green's cancer has been caused by **genetic** factors?

....

....

b) What evidence is there that Mr Green's cancer has been caused by his **environment**?

....

....

c) What would you need to do to get a better idea whether this type of cancer is caused by genes or the environment?

....

....

Q5 The following factors are all known to increase peoples **risk** of getting **heart disease**. Tick the boxes to show whether they are usually caused by **genetic** or **environmental** factors.

	Genetic	Environmental
a) Smoking	☐	☐
b) High cholesterol level	☐	☐
c) Being overweight	☐	☐
d) Having a close relative who has died of heart disease	☐	☐
e) A high salt diet	☐	☐

Top Tips: The reason why you look different to your brother or sister, or pretty much anyone else out there is because of variation. Variation occurs in two stages, firstly when the sex cells (sperm and egg cells) are formed and then when the sperm and egg join together at fertilisation.

Module B1 — You and Your Genes

Single Gene Inheritance

Q1 A plant has two alleles for **flower colour**. The allele for red flowers (**R**) is **dominant** over the allele for white flowers (**r**).

a) The genetic diagram below shows what happens when a plant with the alleles **Rr** is crossed with a plant with the alleles **rr**. In the spaces below, write what colour the offspring could be.

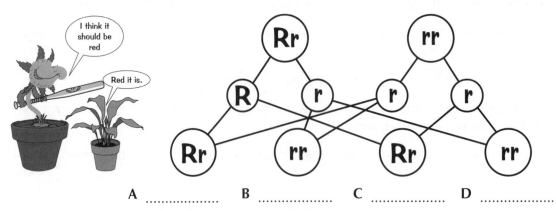

A .... B .... C .... D ....

b) What is the chance of the offspring having **red** flowers?

....

c) Why isn't it possible to draw a similar genetic diagram for **height** in humans?

....

Q2 The ability to roll the tongue is controlled by a **single gene** — rolling (**R**) is **dominant** to non-rolling (**r**). Use this information to complete the following sentences by circling the correct word(s).

Sandeep is unable to roll his tongue. This is caused by a **recessive** / **dominant** allele so will show up when there **is one copy** / **are two copies**. This means that Sandeep must have the alleles **rr** / **Rr** / **RR**.

Q3 In cats, the allele for black fur (B) is **dominant** over the allele for brown fur (b). Two black cats, Jasper and Belle, have a litter of kittens. Most are black, but one is brown. Tick the boxes to show whether the following statements are **true** or **false**.

	True	False
a) All the brown kittens have the alleles bb.	☐	☐
b) Jasper's alleles are BB.	☐	☐
c) Belle's alleles are Bb.	☐	☐
d) The brown kitten must be a mutation — all the kittens should be black.	☐	☐

Brown fur is recessive — for one of the kittens to have brown fur both of the parents must have a copy of the allele.

Single Gene Inheritance

Q4 | Whether or not a person's **eyebrows** join together is controlled by a **single gene**. The allele for separate eyebrows **(S)** is **dominant** to joined eyebrows **(s)**. The family tree below shows how the gene is passed from one generation to the next.

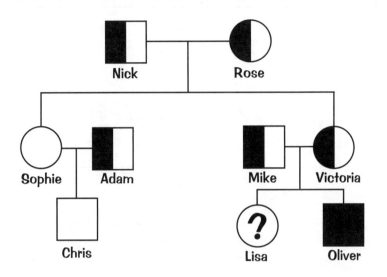

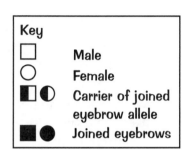

Key
- ☐ Male
- ○ Female
- ◨ ◖ Carrier of joined eyebrow allele
- ■ ● Joined eyebrows

a) Who in the family has joined eyebrows?

....

b) Who in the family is a **carrier** of the joined eyebrows allele?

....

c) It is unknown whether **Lisa** will have joined or separate eyebrows. The genetic diagram below shows what could happen when Mike's alleles are combined with Victoria's alleles.

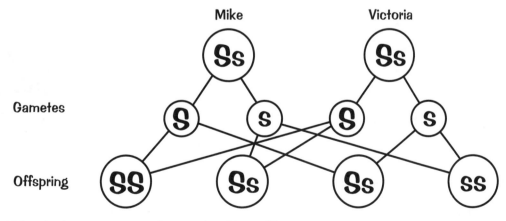

What is the percentage chance that Lisa will:

i) be a **carrier** of the joined eyebrow allele? Circle the correct answer.

        0%   25%   50%   75%   100%

ii) **have** joined eyebrows? Circle the correct answer.

        0%   25%   50%   75%   100%

Clones

Q1   Fill in the blanks in the following passage using the words below.

| genes | parent | single | genetically | two | asexual |

Clones are organisms that are .... identical. They can be produced

naturally by .... reproduction. Many bacteria reproduce in this way,

a .... bacterium can split into .... new individuals.

There is only one .... so all of the offspring will have exactly the

same .... as the parent.

Q2   Mrs Carter had an unusual plant in her garden. One of her neighbours, Mr Richards, liked the plant so Mrs Carter gave him an **offshoot**. Another neighbour, Mrs Evans, also liked the plant, Mrs Carter gave her some **seeds** she had collected from her plant.

a)   Has the offshoot been formed by **sexual** or **asexual** reproduction?

....

b)   The **seeds** Mrs Carter gives Mrs Evans have been produced by **sexual** reproduction.
Will the plants Mrs Evans grows be genetically identical Mrs Carter's?

....

c) **i)** Do you think that the plants that Mr Richards grows will be genetically identical to those in Mrs Carters garden?

....

      ii) Explain your answer to part i).

....

....

Q3   **Identical twins** are natural **clones**.

a)   Explain how the way they are formed makes identical twins genetically identical.

....

....

b)   If identical twins are genetically identical what must be responsible for any differences between them?

....

Genetic Disorders

Q1 Tick the boxes to show whether the following statements about **cystic fibrosis** are **true** or **false**.

		True	False
a)	It is a genetic disorder.	☐	☐
b)	It is caused by a faulty allele.	☐	☐
c)	It is contagious.	☐	☐
d)	It can be inherited.	☐	☐

Q2 The family tree below shows a family with a history of **cystic fibrosis**. Both Libby and Anne are pregnant. They know the sexes of their babies but not whether they have the disorder.

Key
☐ Male
○ Female
■ ◖ Carrier
■ ● Sufferer

a) It is possible to have **one** allele for cystic fibrosis, yet not know it because you show no symptoms. How is this possible?

....

....

b) What is the percentage chance that Libby's baby will:

i) be a **carrier** of the disease? Circle the correct answer.

   0%   25%   50%   75%   100%

ii) **have** the disease? Circle the correct answer.

   0%   25%   50%   75%   100%

Sketch out a genetic diagram if it helps.

c) What is the percentage chance that Anne's baby will:

i) be a **carrier** of the disease? Circle the correct answer.

   0%   25%   50%   75%   100%

ii) **have** the disease? Circle the correct answer.

   0%   25%   50%   75%   100%

Cystic Fibrosis

d) Describe the **symptoms** someone suffering from cystic fibrosis would have.

....

Genetic Disorders

Q3   Derek has recently been diagnosed with **Huntington's disorder**.

a)   List three symptoms of Huntington's disorder.

....

b)   It is possible for a Derek to pass the disorder on to his children unknowingly. Why is this?

....

....

c)   Derek has two children.

i)   What is the chance of each child inheriting the disorder?

....

ii) If one of his children tests positive for the disorder, what is the chance of his other child also suffering from the disorder?

....

Q4   The table compares the **survival rates** of those born in 1960 and 1980 suffering from **disorder A**. Use this data to show what conclusions can be drawn by placing a tick in the correct column.

Year of birth	Percentage of sufferers surviving to the age of:					
	5	10	15	20	25	30
1960	72	58	47	39	31	24
1980	89	85	79	74	69	—

Conclusion	Data indicates it is correct	Data indicates it is incorrect	Data provides no information
People born with disorder A in 1980 are living longer than people with disorder A born in 1960.			
In 1980 a greater percentage of sufferers died before the age of ten than in 1960.			
53% of sufferers born in 1960 died before the age of 15.			
People born in the year 2000 have a greater chance of living until 40 than those born in 1990.			
Fewer sufferers are dying before the age of ten because of improvements in health care.			
Approximately twice as many people born in 1980 survived to the age of 25 than those born in 1960.			
1970 showed the highest percentage of people dying from the disorder before the age of 5.			

Genetic Testing

Q1 Rod and Jane are currently undergoing **IVF treatment**.

a) What do the letters IVF stand for? ....

b) Give one reason why genetic screening may be carried out when a couple are undergoing IVF.

....

c) The fetus is tested using **amniocentesis**. What does this involve?

....

d) Give one possible danger of this procedure.

....

e) Approximately 1 in every 2500 babies born in the UK will have cystic fibrosis. About 600 000 babies are born in the UK each year. How many would you expect to have cystic fibrosis?

....

Q2 Some people **object** to genetic testing. Complete the table to show if the issues are objections based on **fact** or **opinion**.

Objection	Fact	Opinion
The tests are not 100% reliable		
It is wrong to tamper with nature		
There is a risk of miscarriage		
A positive result will cause the parents to choose to have an abortion		

Q3 **Children** and **adults** can be genetically tested to give an **indication** of their risk of getting a disease later in life. Two diseases that can be tested for are **colorectal cancer** and **ovarian cancer**. Use the information about the two diseases to say if the statements below are **true** or **false**.

- Genetic testing for colorectal cancer identifies people with a high risk of getting the disease. These people can then have regular screening for the cancer, which increases their chances of survival considerably.

- Less than half the women identified by genetic testing, as at risk of ovarian cancer actually go on to develop the disease. There is no effective screening for ovarian cancer and the only thing that can be done to remove the risk is to have the ovaries removed.

True False

a) The test for ovarian cancer is not very reliable. ☐ ☐

b) Testing for a high risk of getting colorectal cancer is more useful than testing for a risk of ovarian cancer because there is no effective screening method for ovarian cancer. ☐ ☐

c) The only way to remove the risk of ovarian cancer is to remove the ovaries. ☐ ☐

Gene Therapy

Q1   Tick the boxes to show whether the following
statements about gene therapy are **true** or **false**.

		True	False
a)	It can only be carried out on unborn babies.	☐	☐
b)	It is readily available for a wide range of disorders.	☐	☐
c)	It is 100% reliable.	☐	☐
d)	It works by inserting a healthy copy of a gene.	☐	☐

Q2   Complete the passage using the words below.

repeated	target	leg	virus	cystic fibrosis	days
seconds	airways	healthy	bacteria	the common cold	

One potential application of gene therapy is the treatment of ....
This involves using a .... to deliver a ....
copy of the gene into the patient's .... But, there are some
problems with the treatment. The effects of the treatment wear off after a couple of
.... Some people also fear the treatment might affect cells other
than the .... cells.

Q3   Some people **inherit** faulty versions of genes that predispose them to **breast cancer**.

a)   Describe how gene therapy could be used to help these people.

....

....

b)   Why can't this be done at the moment?

....

....

c)   Why would it be possible for someone who had this treatment to still get breast cancer?

....

Q4   Place a tick in the correct box to indicate whether the following statements are **fact** or **opinion**.

	Fact	Opinion
It will be a few years before some gene therapies can be used		
Gene therapy could be used to prevent inherited breast cancer		
The procedures in gene therapy could have risks we don't yet know about		
Some people see gene therapy as playing god		

Stem Cells

Q1   Tick the boxes to show whether the following statements are **true** or **false**.

		True	False
a)	Most cells in your body are specialised to carry out a specific role.	☐	☐
b)	Differentiation is when a cell grows uncontrollably.	☐	☐
c)	Cells that are specialised are called stem cells.	☐	☐
d)	Stem cells are found in early embryos.	☐	☐
e)	Cells of multicellular organisms become specialised during early development of the organism.	☐	☐

Q2   Stem cells have the potential to **cure** many **diseases**.

a)   Give an example of a disease that can be treated using **adult** stem cells and say where the stem cells come from.

....

....

b)   Researchers are more interested in stem cells from **early human embryos**. Why is this?

....

c)   In order to get a culture of one specific type of cell, researchers need to control the differentiation. How do they do this?

....

Q3   Give one argument in **favour** and one argument **against** using stem cells from embryos.

For: ....

....

Against: ....

....

Q4   In **diabetics**, the insulin producing cells in the pancreas can be **damaged**. Explain how **stem cells** could be used to help diabetics.

....

....

....

Science and Ethics

Q1 Read the passage and answer the questions that follow.

Genetic testing of unborn babies reaches an all time high

Genetic testing can carried out during IVF and only embryos without the faulty gene are implanted into the mother's womb. Fetuses in the mother's womb can also be tested giving parents the option to terminate the pregnancy.

Scientists have found the faulty version of the gene that causes disorder Z (a degenerative nervous system disorder) and have been quick to develop a test for it. The test has been offered since 2000. The graph on the right shows the number babies born with disease Z in country A since the test was introduced.

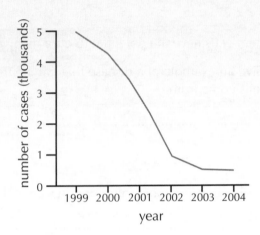

Genetic testing is not without its risks. One method of testing unborn babies is called amniocentesis — fluid from around the fetus (containing fetal cells) is extracted with a syringe and tested. If amniocentesis is carried out there is about a 1% chance of miscarriage.

Some people are against any kind of genetic testing. They think it implies that people with a genetic disorder are inferior to the 'genetically healthy'. Issues are also raised about what action to take if the result of the test is positive. Should the fetus be terminated? — Some people think that they shouldn't because they have a right to life. Other people think that they should as they might suffer their whole lives and might be a burden to their family.

Some people also think that genetic testing for diseases is a 'slippery slope' towards selecting for non-health related characteristics, e.g. eye colour. It may be possible in the future to test for the intelligence of babies before they are born. However, there are a lot of genes involved in the inheritance of intelligence and the environment has a big part to play in developing it. At the moment scientists can only test for single genes.

Science and Ethics

a) For country A:

    i) How many babies were born with disorder Z in the year **before** the test was introduced?

    ii) Describe the **trend** shown in the graph.

    iii) Suggest a **reason** for the trend shown in the graph.

b) **i)** What method can be used to test unborn babies?

    ii) If **4000** fetuses were tested for disorder Z using this method how many **miscarriages** would you expect? Circle the correct answer.

        4   **40**   **400**

c) A couple test their unborn baby for disorder Z and it is found to carry the faulty version of the gene, which means it will have the disorder. What two things can the parents choose to do?

    1.

    2.

d) The article asks, "Should the fetus be terminated?".
Is this a question that can be addressed using a **scientific approach**? Explain your answer.

e) No genetic test is 100% accurate.

    i) Suggest what factors might affect the accuracy of a test result.

    ii) What implications could an inaccurate test result have?

Top Tips: In the exam the article could be about pretty much anything, but all of the information you need to answer the questions will be in the article or you'll have covered it in class.

Module B1 — You and Your Genes

Module C1 — Air Quality

The Atmosphere

Q1 The atmosphere is a **mixture** of gases.

a) Draw a line from each gas to its relative proportion in the atmosphere.

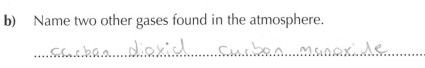

Nitrogen — 1%

Oxygen — 78%

Argon — 21%

b) Name two other gases found in the atmosphere.

...... carbon dioxid carbon monoxide ....

Q2 Complete the following passage by choosing from the words below.

aluminium   climate change   argon   variable   oxides   human activity

constant   concentrations   dioxide   pollutant   asthma

Data collected from various parts of the world has shown that the

...... concentrations ...... of nitrogen, oxygen and ...... argon ...... in the

atmosphere are fairly ...... constant .... Over recent times

...... Pollutant ...... gases such as carbon dioxide, carbon monoxide, sulfur

...... dioxide ...... and nitrogen ...... oxides ...... have been added to

the atmosphere by the effects of ...... climate change human activity ...... — mainly the

burning of fuels. These pollutants can affect humans directly, causing breathing

problems like ...... asthma .... They can also affect us indirectly — there's

a scientific consensus that some pollutants are leading to ...... climate change ....

Q3 a) Tick the boxes to show whether the following statements are **true** or **false**.

	True	False
i) Most of the fuels we burn in cars are carbohydrates.		✓
ii) Hydrocarbons contain only carbon and hydrogen atoms.	✓	
iii) Diesel fuel is a compound of hydrocarbons.	✓	
iv) Pollutants can cause acid rain.	✓	

b) Write corrected versions for the two false statements.

...... they re mixtures of hydrocarbons ......

The Atmosphere

Q4   Circle the correct letter for each of the following questions.

a) Daniel collected some air samples from his home town and analysed them for pollutants. Which one of the following number of samples would give him the most accurate results?

   A 20 samples   B 2 samples   C 8 samples   D 40 samples *(circled)*

b) Any solid bits he finds are likely to be:

   A hydrogen   B carbon *(circled)*   C sulfur   D chlorine

c) When air samples from the same area were analysed for carbon dioxide the following results were obtained. Which result is anomalous?

   A 381 ppm   B 380 ppm   C 365ppm *(circled)*   D 380ppm

d) Which one of the following is unlikely to be the result of climate change?

   A changing sea levels   B more UV light reaching Earth *(circled)*   C more droughts   D more hurricanes

Q5   Scientists at the Mauna Loa observatory in Hawaii have been measuring **atmospheric carbon dioxide** levels for over **60 years**. The graph below shows how the level of carbon dioxide in the atmosphere changed from 1968 to 2000.

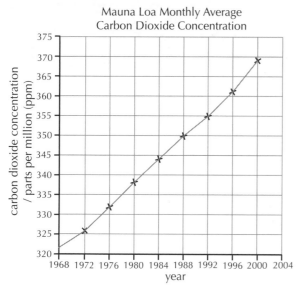

a) What was the concentration of carbon dioxide in 1972?

   325

b) By how much did the carbon dioxide concentration increase between 1976 and 1996?

   29

c) All the data in the graph is **reliable**. What does this mean?

   thus the carbon dioxide levels concentration levels are rising increasing the severity global warming

---

Top Tips: I don't know if you've ever noticed, but if you blow your nose after a day out in a big city, then your snot will probably be **black**. That's from all the little bits of carbon floating about in the air — just one of the many types of pollutant that can be found in the Earth's atmosphere.

Chemical Reactions

Q1   Complete the sentences by circling the **correct** word in each pair.

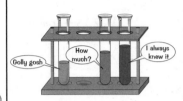

Burning / **Melting** is an example of a chemical reaction — atoms are

rearranged / **destroyed** to make new substances.

When a hydrocarbon is burnt / **dissolved**, carbon reacts with

oxygen / **nitrogen** in the air to make carbon dioxide.

The hydrogen atoms in a hydrocarbon combine with **argon** / oxygen

atoms in the air to make water / **carbohydrates**.

Q2   Gwyneth draws the diagram below to show the reaction between **hydrogen** (H_2) and **oxygen** (O_2).

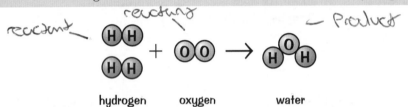

reactant   reactant   ← Product

HH
    + OO → HOH
HH

hydrogen   oxygen   water

a)   Label the reactants and products.

b) i)   Fill in the table to show how many atoms of hydrogen and oxygen there are in the reactants and products shown in the diagram.

	reactants	products
number of hydrogen atoms	4	2
number of oxygen atoms	2	1

ii)   What is wrong with the diagram? Explain what Gwyneth should do to correct it.

It is not balanced

Q3   Coal is largely made up of carbon and hydrogen. The carbon in coal burns in oxygen to produce **carbon dioxide**.

a)   Describe how the properties of **carbon dioxide** differ from those of the reactants.

....

....

b)   Draw a diagram of the atoms and molecules showing the reaction when carbon burns in oxygen.

c)   Explain why other pollutant gases (e.g. sulfur dioxide) are also produced when coal is burnt.

....

Air Pollution — Carbon

Q1   Tick the boxes to show whether the following statements are **true** or **false**.

		True	False
a)	Fossil fuels contain large amounts of the element calcium.		✓
b)	Fossil fuels are formed from the remains of dead plants and animals.	✓	
c)	Carbon trioxide is formed when fossil fuels burn in lots of oxygen.		✓
d)	Particles of soot are produced when carbon-based fuels burn, especially in a limited amount of oxygen.		✓

Q2   Circle the letter next to the diagram that represents:

a)   carbon monoxide

A   B   C   D

b)   carbon dioxide

A   B   C   D

Q3   Fossil fuels have a **variety** of different **uses**.

a)   Explain why we burn fossil fuels.

....

b)   What is the main carbon-containing product when a fossil fuel is burnt in plenty of oxygen?

....

c)   When petrol is burnt in a car engine, the amount of oxygen available is limited.
How does this affect what substances are produced by the reaction?

....

....

Q4   Excess carbon dioxide in the atmosphere causes **environmental damage**.

a)   What process do green plants use to remove carbon dioxide from the atmosphere?

....

b)   Describe how the world's oceans can affect atmospheric carbon dioxide levels.

....

c)   Explain why increasing carbon dioxide levels are causing the polar ice caps to melt.

....

....

Air Pollution — Carbon

Q5 The graph shows how the **carbon monoxide** concentrations in the air changed during a typical Monday in a large city.

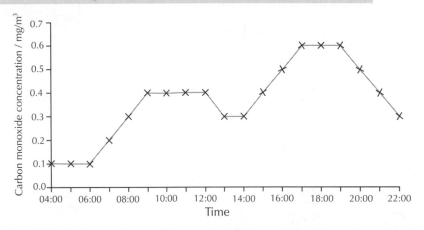 

a) For each point on the graph, 20 air samples were taken. The value on the graph is the **average** of these 20 readings. Why was this done?

....

....

b) On Monday mornings between 06:00 and 09:00 the **traffic** is increasingly heavy.

    i) Is there a correlation between carbon monoxide concentration and the level of traffic? Use the graph to explain your answer.

    ....

    ....

    ii) Do you think that an increase in one factor causes an increase in the other? Explain your answer.

    ....

    ....

c) Would this data set convince the scientific community of a link between traffic levels and carbon monoxide concentration?

....

....

d) Suggest why more drivers might experience headaches during their evening journey.

....

....

Top Tips: The problem with atmospheric pollutants is that they just stay there, causing problems. And we're constantly adding more — which isn't going to make things any better.

Module C1 — Air Quality

Air Pollution — Sulfur and Nitrogen

Q1 Complete the following passage using the words below.

You may have to use some words more than once.

dioxide   sulfur   killing   burnt   carbon   sulfuric   lakes   oxygen

Coal is a ....-based fuel which commonly contains impurities. The impurity
that causes the biggest problem is .... When the fuel is ....
this impurity reacts with .... to give ....
This is a pollutant, which reacts with moisture in clouds to form .... acid,
causing acid rain. Acid rain can be damaging to the environment causing
.... to become acidic and .... plants and aquatic animals.

Q2 Tick the boxes to show whether the following statements are **true** or **false**.

		True	False
a)	Nitrogen oxides are pollutants formed from impurities in fuels.	☐	☐
b)	Nitrogen reacts with oxygen at high temperatures to form nitrogen oxides.	☐	☐
c)	When nitrogen oxides react with moisture, nitrogenoic acid is formed.	☐	☐
d)	Acid rain can damage structures made of limestone.	☐	☐
e)	Nitrogen dioxide has the formula NO.	☐	☐

Q3 Clare is investigating how the concentration of atmospheric **pollutants** that cause **acid rain** affect the life span of a **limestone** headstone. She carried out an experiment by following these instructions:

The concentration of a solution can be measured in mol/dm^3.

1. Place 25 cm^3 of 0.1 mol/dm^3 acid in a conical flask.
2. Add 1 g of small limestone chips and time how long it takes for them to completely dissolve.
3. Repeat the experiment three times using 0.1 mol/dm^3 acid.
4. Repeat steps 1 – 3 using stronger, 0.2 mol/dm^3, acid instead of 0.1 mol/dm^3 acid.

a) Why did she do the experiment four times at each concentration of acid?

....

b) Why is it a good idea for a second scientist to carry out the experiment?

....

c) What sort of correlation should Clare expect between the concentration of acid and the time taken for the limestone chips to dissolve?

....

....

Reducing Pollution

Q1 Tick the boxes to show whether the following statements are **true** or **false**.

	True	False
a) Fuel oil contains no sulfur.	☐	☐
b) Coal-fired power stations produce carbon particles.	☐	☐
c) Removal of sulfur from natural gas before burning will increase the amount of sulfur dioxide released into the atmosphere.	☐	☐

Q2 **Exhaust emission** checks are part of the **MOT test**. The test centres use a meter to check for **carbon monoxide** and **hydrocarbons**. George's three year old car had the following test results:

	George's car	Maximum level of emissions allowed		
		1st August 1992 - present	1st August 1986 - 31st July 1992	Before 31st August 1986
Carbon monoxide level	0.2%	0.3%	3.5%	4.5%
Hydrocarbon level	4 ppm	200 ppm	1200 ppm	1200 ppm

a) Did George's car pass the emissions test? ....

Any hydrocarbons found in the exhaust haven't been used efficiently.

b) Based on the levels of emissions allowed in the past, would you say that the car was more efficient than a typical car made in 1991? Explain your answer.

....

....

Q3 Cars are a major source of **pollution**, though technological advances could help to **reduce** this.

a) Petrol stations now sell low-sulfur fuel. How could this help to reduce pollution?

....

b) Catalytic converters change nitrogen monoxide into which two gases?

....

c) What is the benefit of a catalytic converter changing carbon monoxide into carbon dioxide?

....

Q4 Some local authorities in the UK have tried to reduce **air pollution** by introducing certain initiatives. For each of the following suggest **how** it will help reduce pollution.

a) Charging people £8 to drive a car into the centre of a major city.

....

....

b) Reduced tax for cars with smaller engines.

....

....

Interpreting Pollution Data

Q1   Read the following passage and answer the questions that follow.

Air pollution — getting to the heart of the matter

A team of scientists from the University of Southern California have found that high levels of pollution (caused by traffic and industry) could trigger atherosclerosis — the narrowing of arteries[1]. Narrowing of the arteries is caused by a thickening of the artery lining. This reduces blood flow in the artery.

Links between narrowed arteries and factors like smoking, obesity and diabetes are well established, but this report provides evidence for a link with air pollution. The study involved 798 people over the age of 40 living in the Los Angeles area. The thickness of the lining of their carotid arteries (the main artery in the neck) was measured using ultrasound.

The scientists also recorded pollution levels around the volunteers' homes. They measured the number of pollutant particles with a diameter of 2.5 micrometres or less. These particles, known as $PM_{2.5}$, are commonly produced by burning fossil fuels, e.g. petrol in cars. The levels of $PM_{2.5}$ were found to range from 5.2 to 26.9 micrograms per cubic metre ($\mu g/m^3$).

[1] Nino Künzli, Michael Jerrett, Wendy J. Mack, Bernardo Beckerman, Laurie LaBree, Frank Gilliland, Duncan Thomas, John Peters, and Howard N. Hodis. Ambient Air Pollution and Atherosclerosis in Los Angeles. Environ Health Perspect 113:201–206 (2005).

The study found that the higher the $PM_{2.5}$ level, the thicker the artery lining. On average, the artery lining was 5.9% thicker for every extra 10 $\mu g/m^3$ of $PM_{2.5}$ particles in the air. The results varied with age and sex, with the strongest link being in women over the age of 60, as shown in figure 1.

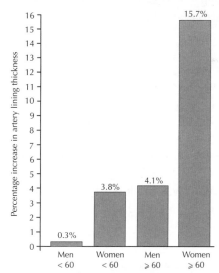

Figure 1. Percentage increase in thickness of artery lining for every 10 $\mu g/m^3$ increase in pollution.

Exactly how air pollution leads to artery narrowing is still unknown. One theory is that air pollution causes the body to produce chemicals that trigger arterial damage. Given that heart disease is now the biggest killer in many developed countries, the findings of this study could have a major influence on government decisions about public health.

Interpreting Pollution Data

a) Atherosclerosis is caused by the build-up of fatty materials in the arteries.

   i) Circle any factors below that have been linked to atherosclerosis.

       measles   smoking   obesity   tallness   hay fever   diabetes

   ii) In which artery did the scientists measure the build-up of fatty materials?

      ....

   iii) How did the scientists measure the thickness of the artery lining?

      ....

b) The scientists measured the levels of $PM_{2.5}$ particles around the volunteers' homes.

   i) What are $PM_{2.5}$ particles?

      ....

      ....

   ii) Describe one cause of $PM_{2.5}$ pollution.

      ....

   iii) What was the lowest concentration of $PM_{2.5}$ recorded in the study?

      ....

c) **i)** Circle the measures that could be used to reduce the amount of pollution produced by cars.

      power steering   catalytic converters   air bags   anti-lock brakes   low sulfur fuels

   ii) For any measures that you circled above, explain how they reduce pollution.

      ....

      ....

      ....

d) Tick the box next to the statement which best describes what the study shows.

   People living in areas of high pollution all suffer from atherosclerosis. ☐

   Only people over the age of 60 will suffer from atherosclerosis. ☐

   The risk of atherosclerosis is higher for people living in high pollution areas. ☐

Interpreting Pollution Data

e) The strongest link between pollution levels and artery narrowing was in women over 60. Women over 60 made up 23.3% of the volunteers.

Look back at the article to find the total number of volunteers.

   i) How many of the volunteers were women over 60?

....

   ii) What **percentage increase** in the thickness of the artery lining was seen in women over 60 years old (for every 10 µg/m³ increase in pollution levels)?

....

   iii) A 62 year old woman living in an area of Los Angeles with a PM$_{2.5}$ pollution level of **8.0 µg/m³** had an artery lining thickness of **100 µm**.

What is the most likely artery lining thickness of a 62 year old woman living in an area of Los Angeles with a PM$_{2.5}$ pollution level of **18 µg/m³**? Circle the correct answer and explain your choice.

      104 µm   116 µm   147 µm   97 µm   200 µm

mine's bigger than yours

....

....

....

f) Some scientists feel that further large-scale studies are needed to assess the health impacts of long-term exposure to air pollution.

   i) Suggest why the study might benefit from extra data.

....

....

   ii) From the study described in the article, is it possible to say that 'air pollution causes atherosclerosis'? Explain your answer.

....

....

Top Tips: Questions like this might seem a bit scary but the key is not to panic. You get the article before the exam so it should be familiar, and you'll be able to answer all the questions using the information in the article or what you've learnt from the rest of the specification.

Module C1 — Air Quality

Sustainable Development

Q1   Read the following passage and answer the questions that follow.

Fuel Cells — the future of sustainability?

A fuel cell is an electrochemical device that combines hydrogen and oxygen to generate electricity. Fuel cells can be produced on any scale to give the desired power output. They have a wide range of applications — the one that interests most people is replacement of the standard car engine. Cars powered by fuel cells are basically electric cars that don't rely on batteries — they generate their own electricity.

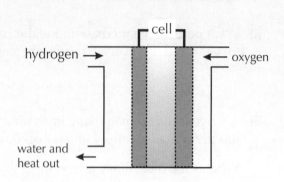

Fuel cells have the potential to reduce pollution.

With the potential to replace traditional petrol and diesel engines, fuel cells have a number of advantages:
- They produce no greenhouse gases (such as carbon dioxide), particulates or nitrogen oxide emissions. In fact the only product is water.
- Cars powered by fuel cells only use energy when they're moving, unlike a traditional car which uses fuel when stationary. Vehicles powered by a hydrogen fuel cell can be three times more efficient than those powered by petrol.
- They're very quiet compared to normal vehicle engines.

One big disadvantage is refuelling. Currently, cars powered by fuel cells can only cover a short distance before they need refuelling. However, a spokesperson for one of the large car manufacturers said that by 2010, they will have designed a fuel cell car that can go as far on a full tank as a petrol car, "without the fuel tank being twice the size of the car."

The key to making fuel cells sustainable lies with the production of the hydrogen fuel. Producing hydrogen needs a lot of energy, and this has to come from renewable energy resources such as solar, wind or biomass — or else it's still causing a lot of environmental damage.

Many fuel cell powered cars are still in early stages of development so it'll be a while before we see whether they make it to mass production.

Many see the hydrogen fuel cell as crucial in a sustainable future. It can not only reduce our dependence on oil, but will also benefit the environment by reducing emissions of greenhouse gases and pollutants that affect our air quality.

Sustainable Development

a) Fuel cells produce electrical energy from hydrogen and oxygen.

   i) Circle the product(s) produced by a fuel cell.

      carbon monoxide   water   methane

   ii) Complete the table about the pollutants produced by an internal combustion engine (a standard car engine).

Pollutant	Environmental problem it causes	Can be reduced by using
CO_2		More efficient engines
	Acid rain	Low sulfur fuel
nitrogen oxides		

   iii) Give two types of pollution that using fuel cells could reduce.

      ....

      ....

b) In the article, the spokesperson for the car manufacturer jokes about the size of the fuel tank needed in a fuel cell powered car.

   i) Suggest why a fuel tank for hydrogen would have to be a lot bigger than a fuel tank for petrol.

      ....

      ....

      ....

   ii) One of the reasons fuel cells are more efficient than petrol engines is because they have no moving parts. Give one other reason why fuel cells are more efficient than a standard car engine.

      ....

c) Suggest why there is a large focus on the use of hydrogen fuel cells to replace the standard car engine.

   ....

   ....

Sustainable Development

d) The fuel cell is seen by many as "crucial in a sustainable future".

    i) What is meant by the term 'sustainable development'?

    ....

    ....

    ii) Give two ways in which the invention of the internal combustion engine (standard car engine) has improved some people's quality of life.

    ....

    ....

    iii) Give one way in which the internal combustion engine has contributed to environmental problems.

    ....

    ....

    iv) Hydrogen fuel cells can produce energy for cars and a range of other applications. How could this help our society to develop sustainably?

    ....

    ....

    ....

    v) Some people argue that fuel cells are not a sustainable technology because energy is needed to produce the hydrogen, and this energy normally comes from burning fossil fuels. How does the article suggest this problem can be overcome?

    ....

    ....

e) The article says that the use of fuel cells will reduce our dependence on oil. In what ways are we dependent on oil?

....

Sure, I could give it up any time. If I really wanted to.

....

....

Top Tips: With an ever increasing world population, the pressure on non-renewable fuel resources is likely to get bigger and bigger. And the more of us that there are, the greater the number of cars producing pollutants, and the more inviting fuel cell powered cars seem...

The Changing Earth

Q1 Rocks in the Earth's crust show that the Earth is **continually changing**.
Match up the processes that help to change the Earth with their definitions.

Erosion

Over time, rock builds up around any dead organisms in the sediment.

Sedimentation

Rocks are continually worn away by the wind and other processes.

Fossilisation

Rocks are squeezed into new formations due to high temperatures and pressures.

Folding

Particles from existing rock are washed away into the sea where they are eventually pressed into new rocks.

Q2 Tick the boxes to show whether the following statements are true or false.

True False

a) If rocks weren't continually recycled to make new mountains, all land would be at sea level. ☐ ☐

b) Mount Everest is continually being worn away by erosion. ☐ ☐

c) Folds in rocks suggest that huge temperatures and pressures have moved the rock in the past. ☐ ☐

d) Although rocks have moved around in the past, this is no longer happening today. ☐ ☐

Q3 Scientists have measured the age of some of Earth's rocks using radioactive dating.
They have found that the oldest are **4 billion years old**. Which of these statements can be deduced from **this evidence alone**? Circle the letter(s) next to the correct answer(s).

A The Universe is 4 billion years old.

B All rocks were formed 4 billion years ago.

C The Earth is at least 4 billion years old.

D The rock cycle has been happening for at least 4 billion years.

Be careful — don't assume anything.

Q4 **Volcanoes** play an important part in shaping the surface of the Earth.

a) How do volcanoes create new rock?

....

b) You can often find fossils in sedimentary rock.
Explain why you wouldn't find fossils in the rock formed by volcanoes.

Think how fossils are formed.

....

....

Observations and Explanations

Q1 Fossils of the **same species** of animal have been found on both sides of the **Atlantic Ocean**.

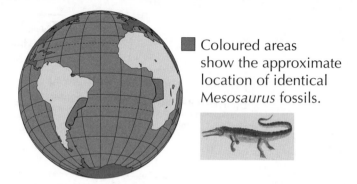

■ Coloured areas show the approximate location of identical *Mesosaurus* fossils.

a) Wegener put forward the theory of **continental drift** to explain how fossils of the same species of animal could be found in two very different places. What did he mean by 'continental drift'?

....

....

b) How does Wegener's theory account for the presence of identical fossils either side of the Atlantic?

....

....

c) Give one other piece of evidence from the diagram that adds weight to Wegener's explanation.

....

Q2 There are many ways for scientists to gather data about the movement of the Earth, e.g. satellites can accurately measure the speeds of various points on the Earth's surface. Decide whether each of the following statements describes **data** or is part of a possible **explanation** of the data.

		Data	Explanation
a)	Parts of the Earth's surface are moving relative to each other.	☐	☐
b)	This 'plate movement' is driven by convection currents in the mantle.	☐	☐
c)	In the past, there was only one large landmass called Pangaea.	☐	☐
d)	The coastlines of continents seem to fit together like a big jigsaw.	☐	☐
e)	New rock is being formed at the bottom of the Atlantic ocean — at the mid-Atlantic ridge.	☐	☐

Observations and Explanations

Q3   Choose from the words given below to complete the passage.

growing continental boundaries collide shrinking supports chains continents fork

In the past, people thought mountains were formed by the Earth's surface cooling and contracting. Wegner suggested that instead, mountains are formed where .... plates .... and crumple. His theory also explains why mountains are usually found in ...., as they form along the .... between colliding continents. Scientists have found that the Himalayas are still ...., which .... Wegner's theory.

Q4   Wegener put forward his theory of continental drift in 1912. However, it wasn't accepted by the scientific community until about 60 years after its publication.

a)   Give one **scientific** reason why the scientific community found it hard to accept that the continents had actually moved apart.

....

b)   What was it about **Wegener himself** that meant geologists had a hard time accepting his ideas?

....

c)   Why did the discovery that the sea floor is moving apart lead to most scientists accepting the theory?

....

Q5   However convincing the evidence in favour of a scientific theory, we can never **prove** the theory right. But only **one** piece of valid evidence can prove it **wrong**. Why is this?

....

....

Top Tips: Science is all about observations and explanations — a scientist sees something happen that isn't predicted by a current theory, so tries to explain why it happens like that. It can be tough to think up new explanations — then you've got to convince everyone else your theory's right.

Module P1 — The Earth in the Universe

The Structure of the Earth

Q1 **Label** this diagram of the Earth, and match up the labels with their **descriptions**.

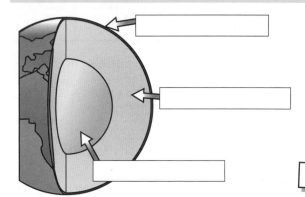

Hot, solid rock that can flow very slowly.

It is only about 20 km thick.

Very dense — consists mainly of iron and nickel.

There are two types: oceanic and continental.

Q2 Choose from the words in this list to complete the paragraph below.

heat   tectonic   mantle   convection   crust   radioactive

.... decay in the Earth's interior produces a lot of

.... , which causes .... currents

to flow in the .... These currents drive the

movement of the Earth's .... plates .

Q3 The table shows the dates on which a particular city was hit by earthquakes.

Date	Magnitude (severity of quake)
12th Dec 1632	6.9
14th Jul 1721	7.2
23rd May 1810	3.8
12th Jan 1812	3.2
12th Aug 1904	8.6
14th Feb 1990	7.4

a) When did the largest earthquake happen?

....

b) Suggest why the 1812 earthquake was unexpected.

....

....

c) Based on the data, for what year would you predict the next earthquake? ....

d) Why is it difficult to predict when an earthquake is going to happen?

....

Q4 **Iceland** is on the **edge** of the Eurasian tectonic plate. The **UK** is further towards the **middle** of the plate. Are earthquakes and volcanoes more likely in the UK or Iceland? Explain your answer.

....

....

Module P1 — The Earth in the Universe

The Solar System

Q1 Many different objects in space can be seen from Earth with the naked eye.

a) The Sun is a star. Why do other stars in the night sky look so much smaller than the Sun?

....

b) Planets and stars can look very similar in the night sky. Stars can be seen because they give out light. Planets do not give out light, so how can they be seen from Earth?

....

c) Why do we only see comets for a very short part of their orbit?

....

Q2 Write down these Solar System objects in order of **increasing size**.

| planet | moon | Sun | comet |

1. ....   2. ....

3. ....   4. ....

Q3 Choose words from the list to fill in the gaps in the following passage.

| objects | star | expanded | Earth | contracted | dust | hot | Sun |

The Solar System started as a cloud of .... and gas. Over

millions of years, this cloud .... under the force of gravity.

At its centre, the cloud became .... enough and dense

enough to form a .... (the ....).

Other parts of the cloud gradually clumped together to become the other

.... in the Solar System.

The Solar System

Q4 Circle the letter next to the correct statement below.

A The Sun and the Earth are roughly the same age.

B The Sun is much younger than the Earth.

C The Sun formed millions of years before the Earth.

Q5 The diagram below shows part of the **Solar System**. It includes some objects which orbit the Sun in between the orbits of Mars and Jupiter.

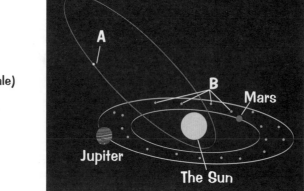

(Diagram not to scale)

a) **i)** What type of object is A?

....

ii) What are the objects labelled B?

....

b) Describe two ways in which the orbit of A is different from the orbits of Mars and Jupiter.

1. ....

2. ....

c) What is object A made from?

....

Top Tips: Who'd have thought a big ball of gas floating around in space could have turned into a star, some planets, asteroids, comets — and the rest of Santa's reindeer (sorry, couldn't resist...). Make sure you know your comets from your asteroids, and where they all hang out.

Danger from Space

Q1 Here is a list of statements about potential **dangers** from space.
Tick the correct boxes to show whether each statement is true or false.

True **False**

a) Every day, dust and tiny rocks from space enter the Earth's atmosphere. ☐ ☐

b) The Earth has been involved in collisions with very large objects from space in the past. ☐ ☐

c) Small objects from space often burn up harmlessly in the Earth's atmosphere. ☐ ☐

d) There are fewer craters on the Moon than the Earth because there have been fewer collisions. ☐ ☐

Q2 Choose the correct word(s) from each pair to complete the following passage.

If a **large** / **small** asteroid collided with the Earth, it could cause a huge amount of damage. **Whirlpools** / **Tsunamis** could be formed if the asteroid landed in **an ocean** / **a pond**. On land there could be **fires** / **volcanic eruptions**, and lots of hot rocks and **air** / **dust** would be thrown up into the atmosphere. This could change the Earth's **climate** / **orbit** by blocking out **cosmic rays** / **sunlight**.

Q3 Bob the astronomer is monitoring the path of a nearby asteroid. He calculates that there is a **1 in 50** chance of the asteroid colliding with the Earth in the next ten years.

a) How do astronomers monitor the paths of asteroids?

....

b) What is the chance of the asteroid **not** hitting the Earth in the next ten years?

....

c) Some asteroids with this chance of hitting the Earth would be of no concern. However other asteroids might cause world-wide panic. Explain why.

....

....

....

Danger from Space

Q4 An asteroid impact has been blamed for the **mass extinction** about 65 million years ago.

a) What is meant by a mass extinction?

....

b) Tick the boxes to show whether each statement describes **data** or is part of an **explanation** of data.

Data Explanation

i) A mass extinction occurred 65 million years ago. ☐ ☐

ii) Unusual elements have been found in rocks. ☐ ☐

iii) There are sudden changes in fossil numbers between adjacent layers of rock. ☐ ☐

iv) Asteroid impacts add rare substances to rocks. ☐ ☐

v) An asteroid impact caused the mass extinction 65 million years ago. ☐ ☐

Q5 The table below shows data collected by NASA about asteroids that might collide with the Earth.

Asteroid	Chance of collision with Earth (per million in next 100 years)	Estimated diameter (km)
2006 SF281	2.3	0.020
2006 UO	0.1	0.210
2006 SC	33	0.032
2006 QV89	320	0.030
2006 UD17	0.013	0.740

Courtesy NASA/JPL-Caltech

a) Not all asteroids would do the same amount of damage if they collided with the Earth. Which asteroids would be likely to do the most and least damage if they collided with us?

i) most: ....

ii) least: ....

b) **i)** Which asteroid has the highest risk of a collision? ....

ii) Why is this unlikely to be a problem for us on Earth?

....

Top Tips: If you read 'Danger from Space' and thought **aagghh** alien invasion, then don't worry — this page is just about giant rocks hitting the Earth and causing mass extinctions. If meteors do worry you, just remember this — space is a big place, so the chance of anything hitting Earth is tiny.

Beyond the Solar System

Q1 Complete the sentences below by choosing the correct word(s) from each pair.

  a) The Sun is about **110 / 10** times bigger than the Earth. The diameter of the Milky Way is about 600 **billion / thousand** times the diameter of the Sun.

  b) The distance between the **planets / galaxies** is usually millions of times more than the distance between the stars in **a galaxy / the Universe**.

  c) There are **billions / thousands** of galaxies in the universe, each containing **thousands / billions** of stars.

Q2 The **light-year** is a unit of distance.

  a) What distance does a light-year represent?

  ....

  b) What property of light means that the length of a light-year is constant?

  ....

  What's special about the speed of light in a vacuum?

  c) A nearby star, Sirius, is 8.6 light-years away.
  If Sirius suddenly exploded, how long would it be before we could know?

  ....

Q3 Complete this table using the numbers given below.

Object	Estimated Age	Estimated Diameter
Earth		
Sun		
Milky Way	13.6 billion years	
Universe		

You don't need to know the figures to answer this question.

  5 billion years   5 billion years   13.7 billion years

  150 billion light-years   12 800 km   100 000 light-years   1.4 million km

Q4 Many scientists think there might be life elsewhere in the Universe.
Tick the boxes to show whether each of the following statements is true or false.

True False

  a) Scientists have discovered many planets orbiting nearby stars. ☐ ☐

  b) It is more likely that microscopic life exists on alien planets than that intelligent life does. ☐ ☐

  c) There is nothing special about Earth's location that allows it to support life. ☐ ☐

Looking into Space

Q1   Some stars look **brighter** than others in the night sky.

a)   What two factors affect how bright a star looks to us from Earth?

1. ....

2. ....

b)   When observing the light from stars, astronomers often complain of light pollution. What is light pollution and why is it a problem?

....

....

Q2   The diagram shows two photographs of the same part of the night sky. The photographs were taken 6 months apart.

a)   Two of the stars (labelled A and B) appear to have moved, while the rest have stayed in the same places. What does this tell us about stars A and B, and why?

5th January   5th July

....

....

b)   Which of the two stars is closer to Earth — star A or star B? Give a reason for your answer.

....

c)   Astronomers can use stars' apparent movement (parallax) to calculate the distance to nearby stars fairly accurately. There is more uncertainty in the measurement of distances to more distant stars. Explain why.

....

Q3   When we look into space, we see things as they were in the past.

a)   Explain why we are seeing stars as they were in the past.

....

b)   SETI is an organisation that searches for extraterrestrial intelligence by looking for **radio signals** transmitted from other planets. Explain why aliens living **200 light-years** away would be unable to detect **us** yet using the same technique.

The world's first radio station began broadcasting in 1897.

....

....

The Life Cycle of Stars

Q1 The Sun will pass through several stages in its life. Write these four stages in the right order.

stable phase   white dwarf   red giant   protostar

....

Q2 Complete the paragraph below about the formation of the Sun by choosing the correct word(s) from each pair.

> The Sun formed from a cloud of **dust and gas / protostars**. This cloud
> **expanded / contracted** under the force of **friction / gravity**, which made the
> centre of the cloud **heat up / cool down**. Eventually the **temperature / pressure**
> was high enough for **fission / fusion** reactions to take place, joining together
> **sulphur / hydrogen** to form **helium / carbon**. These reactions give out massive
> amounts of **light / antimatter** and heat. This process is still happening today.

Q3 Scientists have discovered over 100 elements that make up everything in the Universe.

a) How were the elements heavier than helium made?

....

b) What does this suggest about where the elements that make up the
Earth and everything on it have come from?

....

Q4 The life cycle of a star can take billions of years.

Astronomers discovered the different stages in the life cycles of stars by studying many stars.
Would this discovery have been possible if there was only one star in the sky? Explain your answer.

....

....

....

40

The Life of the Universe

Q1 Here are some statements about the expansion of the Universe. Tick the boxes to show whether each statement describes **data** or is part of an **explanation**.

Data Explanation

a) Most galaxies are moving away from us. ☐ ☐

b) The Universe is expanding. ☐ ☐

c) The Universe started from a single point. ☐ ☐

Q2 Many cosmologists believe that the Universe began with the Big Bang.

a) Briefly describe the Big Bang theory.

....

....

b) How many years ago do cosmologists think the Big Bang happened? ....

Q3 The **eventual fate** of the Universe depends on its current rate of expansion and how quickly the expansion slows down.

a) Which of these quantities determines how quickly the expansion of the Universe slows down? Circle the correct answer.

Friction in the Universe   Temperature of the Universe   Mass of the Universe

b) This quantity is very hard to measure. Choose the correct word from each pair to explain why.

We're not sure how much **dark** / **light** matter there is in the Universe. The only way to detect it is to observe how it affects the **temperature** / **movement** of things we can see.

Q4 The graph below illustrates two possible **fates** of the Universe.

a) On the graph, label when the Big Bang occurred.

b) Use the graph to describe the two predicted fates of the Universe.

A ....

B ....

c) What does line B predict will happen at time C?

....

Module P1 — The Earth in the Universe

The Scientific Community

Q1 Complete this paragraph about scientific theories by choosing the correct word(s) from each pair.

When a new scientific **journal** / **theory** is put forward it has to explain the current **evidence** / **technology**. However, a good theory also makes **assumptions** / **predictions** about measurements that **have already** / **haven't yet** been made. Often we have to wait until **technology** / **a scientist** is **clever** / **advanced** enough to make these measurements. A new theory tends to be **accepted** / **rejected** once its predictions are **confirmed** / **sensible**.

Q2 Number these statements 1 – 6 to put them in the order in which they happened.

☐ Two rival theories were put forward to explain the evidence — the Big Bang theory and the Steady State theory.

☐ Edwin Hubble discovered that the Universe is expanding.

☐ Most scientists believe the Big Bang theory.

☐ The Big Bang theory predicted leftover background radiation from the initial explosion, but the Steady State theory didn't.

☐ Scientists believed the Universe was static and unchanging.

☐ The 'cosmic microwave background radiation' was discovered by accident.

Q3 Before scientific measurements and explanations are accepted by the scientific community, they are usually published in a peer reviewed journal.

a) What is a peer reviewed journal?

....

b) The peer review process helps to make sure that published data is reliable and valid. Explain what is meant by 'reliable data'.

....

Top Tips: Peer review is all about safety in numbers — if only one scientist believes something, he could just be making it up for a laugh, but if loads of scientists think it's true then there's likely to be something in it. Most scientists now accept the Big Bang theory.

Microorganisms and Disease

Q1 Disease in humans can be caused by **microorganisms**.

a) Name **four** types of microorganism.

1. ....   2. ....

3. ....   4. ....

b) Define the term **pathogen**.

....

Q2 Circle the correct word in each pair to complete the passage below.

Many bacteria can cause an infection when they cross natural barriers and enter the body.

The bacteria then start to **reproduce / die** — this can happen quickly because the conditions in the

body are **warm / dark**. When lots of bacteria are present, they start to cause **symptoms / growth**.

This can be due to bacteria producing poisons called **antibodies / toxins**, which can damage the

body's **blood / cells**. Microorganisms can **never / sometimes** damage cells directly.

Q3 Draw lines to match the body's **natural barriers** to infection with their correct descriptions.

Sweat

Tears

Stomach acid

Skin

can kill bacteria in food and water to stop them spreading through your body.

forms an extra protective layer over the skin.

provides a physical barrier to stop microorganisms from getting into your body.

contain chemicals that can kill bacteria.

Q4 An experiment was carried out to investigate the **growth rate** of a bacterium that causes a disease in humans. The experiment was carried out at 37 °C.

a) **Symptoms** of the disease appear when the number of bacteria reach 100 000 per cm³. Using the graph, state how long after infection symptoms would start to appear.

....

b) Suggest a reason why the experiment was carried out at 37 °C.

....

The Immune System

Q1 Draw lines to match the descriptions with the correct terms.

A unique molecule found on the surface of cells.

A molecule that binds to invading microbes to help fight an infection.

Antibody

Antigen

Q2 What is the role of the immune system?

....

Q3 Tick the correct boxes to show whether these statements are **true** or **false**.

		True	False
a)	Every type of invading microorganism has unique molecules on its surface.	☐	☐
b)	When white blood cells come across a foreign cell they start to produce antigens.	☐	☐
c)	Antibodies are not specific to a microorganism.	☐	☐
d)	Some white blood cells can engulf microorganisms and digest them.	☐	☐

Q4 Beth had **mumps** when she was a child. If she is exposed to the pathogen again her body will fight the infection much **quicker**. Put a tick next to the statement that explains why this is.

☐ She is healthier now, than when she was a child.

☐ Beth's body has a 'memory' of the antigen on the pathogen and can quickly produce lots of antibodies if she is infected with the same pathogen again.

☐ She is less likely to be exposed to the pathogen.

Q5 Two friends, Mahmood and Chris had a test to see if they needed to be immunised against tuberculosis (TB). The test measured whether they were **already immune** to TB (i.e. if they had enough antibodies specific to TB in their blood). The results showed that Mahmood had a high level of TB antibodies in his blood but Chris did not. It was recommended that Mahmood did not have the TB vaccination, but that Chris should have it.

a) Explain why Chris needed the vaccination and Mahmood did not.

....

b) Underline a possible reason why Mahmood and Chris had such different levels of antibodies in their blood.

Mahmood was healthier than Chris.   Mahmood had a higher blood level of antigens.

Mahmood had been in contact with the TB microorganism before.

Vaccination

Q1   Complete the passage below using the words provided.

antigens	injecting	harmless	antibodies	microorganisms

Vaccination usually involves .... dead or inactive ....

into the blood. These still carry the same .... as the active

microorganism. This means your body produces .... to attack them,

even though the microorganisms are ....·.

Q2   Tick the correct boxes to show whether these statements are **true** or **false**.   **True**   **False**

a)   If you become infected with a microorganism that you have been
vaccinated against, you won't have the specific antibodies in your blood.   ☐   ☐

b)   If you're infected by a pathogen that you've been vaccinated against,
you can normally get rid of all the pathogens before they reach a level
that makes you ill.   ☐   ☐

c)   Vaccines are always completely safe.   ☐   ☐

Q3   Some microorganisms can **change** very **quickly**.

a)   Circle the correct word(s) in each pair to complete the sentences below.

When some microorganisms reproduce they can undergo random changes.

This means that the next generation is **slightly different** / **identical** to the previous one.

It's **easy** / **hard** to develop vaccines for these kinds of microorganisms because

the changes can lead to them having different **antigens** / **antibodies**.

If you've been vaccinated against one strain of the microorganism and then

it changes, your immune system has to recognise the **old** / **new** antigens.

New vaccines need to be developed regularly.

b)   Name a disease caused by a virus that can undergo this type of change very quickly.

....

Top Tips: Vaccination is a really effective way of controlling the spread of a disease. There's a
small amount of risk involved as the pathogen itself is injected — don't worry side effects are pretty rare.

Vaccination

Q4 A **course of vaccination** against **disease B** consists of three injections at 5-week intervals, followed by a booster injection 5 years later. The graph shows the average level of antibodies in the patients' blood over the course of the programme.

a) Explain why the level of antibodies can be used to measure immunity to a disease.

....

....

b) Using the graph, explain why:

i) **Three** injections are needed initially.

....

ii) A **booster** injection is needed after 5 years.

....

Q5 A **vaccination programme** was introduced in a country to stop the spread of a **disease A**. Parents were advised to have their children vaccinated at the age of 3. Two years later, a survey was done to see the effects of the vaccination programme. The results obtained are shown below.

> **Of the children vaccinated, 11% had developed the disease.**
>
> **Of the non-vaccinated children, 40% had developed the disease.**
>
> **Of the vaccinated children, 10% suffered side effects.**
>
> **In 3% of children, the side effects of the vaccination were very serious.**

a) If there were **50** children vaccinated against disease A in this programme calculate how many suffered side effects?

....

b) Explain why vaccines are never considered to be completely safe.

....

....

Vaccination — Pros and Cons

Q1 Read the passage below and answer the questions that follow.

The MMR Vaccine in the Spotlight

The Government's Health Department is concerned about a possible measles epidemic as parents continue to resist having their children vaccinated against the disease with the MMR vaccine. The graph below shows the number of measles cases in the UK between 1999 and 2004.

The vaccine is given to children when they're around 13 months old and protects them against three diseases — measles, mumps and rubella. Mumps can cause meningitis, sterility in men and deafness. Rubella causes little harm unless it's caught in the early stage of pregnancy, when it can cause severe problems in the developing baby. Measles is the most serious of the three diseases as it can lead to pneumonia, fits, and even death.

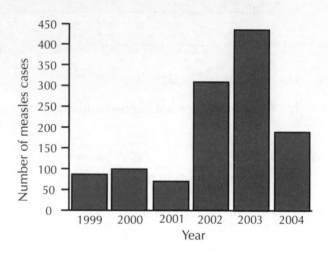

The number of children being vaccinated with the MMR vaccine each year decreased following a paper published in 1998, which suggested a possible link between the MMR vaccine and the brain condition autism. However, many other studies across the world involving thousands of children have consistently failed to find any link between the vaccination and autism.

The Government's target is for 95% of children to be vaccinated. At present, about 85% are being vaccinated, although this is an increase from a low point of around 80% a few years ago.

Some parents would prefer to have their children vaccinated separately against each disease rather than all at once. This is not recommended by the medical authorities for the following reasons:

1. The separate vaccines have not been tested and licensed in this country.

2. It requires more visits to a surgery and there is a greater likelihood that people will forget.

3. The child has to have three times as many injections.

4. The separate vaccines have been shown to be less effective in provoking an immune response.

The MMR vaccine, like all others, can produce unpleasant side effects in some individuals. Scientists cannot categorically prove that there is no link whatsoever between MMR and autism, as some people demand, but all the evidence suggests that any medical risks of having a child vaccinated with MMR are much less than leaving the child unvaccinated.

Page 47

Vaccination — Pros and Cons

a) Suggest why some parents resist having their children vaccinated with the MMR vaccine.

....

....

b) Circle the disease (that is vaccinated against using MMR) that is thought to be the **most serious**.

Mumps   Measles   Rubella

c) **i)** Describe the main trends shown in the bar chart.

....

....

ii) How does the number of cases of measles in 2004 approximately compare with that in 2001?

Four times as many in 2004   Twice as many in 2004

Six times as many in 2004   Three times as many in 2004

iii) Suggest a possible reason for the change in the number of measles cases **after 2001**.

....

....

d) What percentage of children still need to be vaccinated for the Government to reach its target?

....

e) Give an argument **against** forcing the whole population to be vaccinated.

....

....

f) Four reasons are given against the use of separate vaccines for measles, mumps and rubella. Of these, which one do you think parents would be **most** concerned about. Give a reason for your answer.

Think about how we know that vaccines are safe.

....

....

Module B2 — Keeping Healthy

Antibiotics

Q1   From the sentences below circle the correct description of an **antibiotic**.

A chemical produced by white blood cells.

A medicine that helps to get rid of symptoms of disease.

A chemical that kills all microorganisms.   A drug that kills bacteria and fungi.

Q2   Currently, there is a lot of concern about the appearance of **superbugs** — microorganisms that are resistant to most antibiotics. Put a tick next to any of the actions that could help prevent the appearance of superbugs.

☐   Doctors should avoid prescribing antibiotics for minor ailments if patients can do without them.

☐   Scientists should try to invent new antibiotics.

☐   Doctors should try and avoid using the same antibiotic too often.

☐   Patients should not go to the doctor so much.

Q3   The graph shows the number of bacteria Y in Gary's blood during a two-week course of **antibiotics**.

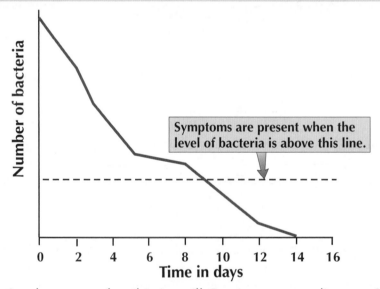

a)   How long after starting the course of antibiotics will Gary's symptoms disappear? ....

b)   Complete the passage below choosing from the words provided.

reproduce	population	finish	species	immune system

It's important for Gary to .... his full course of antibiotics as it could help to prevent

the emergence of antibiotic resistant bacteria. If he doesn't, there might be too many resistant

individuals left for his .... to get rid of — they could

.... to create a whole new .... of antibiotic resistant bacteria.

Antibiotics

Q4 Jenny went to the doctor because she had **flu.** The doctor didn't give her any drugs and advised her to stay in bed for a while. Why wouldn't the doctor give her any antibiotics for her condition? Circle the correct answer.

> Flu is caused by a virus and antibiotics do not affect viruses.

> Flu is caused by a lot of different microorganisms so antibiotics can't cure it.

> Flu is caused by a virus — they have evolved to be resistant to antibiotics.

Q5 In 1960, a **new antibiotic** was discovered that was very effective against **disease Z**. Doctors have been prescribing this drug ever since. The graph below shows the number of deaths from disease Z over a number of years.

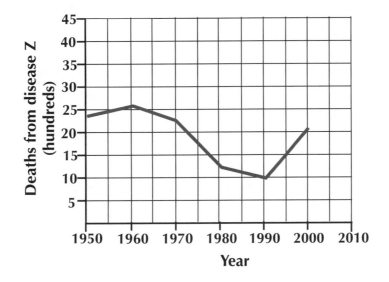

a) Assuming nothing changes, use the graph to **predict** the number of deaths from disease Z in **2010**.

....

b) Suggest a reason for the **fall** in deaths from the disease between 1970 and 1980.

....

c) Suggest a reason for the **sudden rise** in deaths from the disease between 1990 and 2000.

....

Top Tips: Antibiotics are just great but they should be used with care as nobody wants a nasty superbug hanging around, bugging everyone. You need to know how these can develop. So learn it.

Module B2 — Keeping Healthy

Drug Trials

Q1 Complete the passage below choosing from the words provided.

humans	beneficial	safe	harmful	works

Any new drug must be tested to make sure it's .... to use and that it actually .... The way drug trials are structured aims to identify any potentially .... effects before they are given to any ....

Q2 Before a drug can be sold, it is tested on a variety of different cells and organisms. Put the cells and organisms in the order that drugs would be tested on. The first one has been done for you.

- **1** Human cells in a laboratory
- ☐ Sufferers of the disease
- ☐ Healthy human beings
- ☐ Mammals (other than humans)

Q3 Before a drug is tested on sufferers, **clinical trials** are carried out with **healthy volunteers**.

a) Explain why healthy people are used to test the drug before the sufferers.

Think of the effects drugs could have.

....

....

b) What does the term 'clinical trial' mean? Circle the correct answer.

A trial on human beings.

Testing a drug in a laboratory.

The complete processes of testing a drug.

c) If the drug causes no problems whatsoever for the healthy volunteers, can scientists be certain that it is safe to use with sufferers? Explain your answer.

....

....

Drug Trials

Q4 A drug, called JS16, was tested on laboratory rats. The rats were infected with a disease that it was hoped JS16 would cure, and were then given the drug. The results from the next day are shown below.

Level of dosage	% of rats cured	% of rats that died due to side effects
Low	5	0
Medium	65	1
High	77	10

a) What percentage of rats survived the treatment at high doses? ....

b) Do you think it's likely that the drug company will continue with clinical trials in humans? Tick the box next to the correct answer.

☐ Yes. The drug might not cause the same side effects which resulted in the death of laboratory animals.

☐ No. If the side effects caused death in laboratory animals, this will have to be investigated before human trials can start.

Q5 Many people are **against** the use of animals for testing drugs intended for humans.

a) Give one **advantage** of testing drugs on animals.

....

b) Give one **disadvantage** of using animals, when the drug is intended for humans.

....

Q6 Explain why, during trials, the drugs are usually tested on:

a) **Live mammals**.

....

b) **Human cells** grown in a lab.

....

Top Tips: Testing drugs on animals is a very controversial issue. Some people think it's unethical and cruel to use animals in this way. Currently the law states that drugs must be tested on animals before they can be used on humans. A suitable alternative method is needed, before this can change.

The Circulatory System

Q1   Complete the passage using the words provided below.

carbon dioxide	vessels	oxygen	glucose	veins	arteries

> Blood is vital to the working of the body. It is carried around the body in blood
>
> .... The blood is carried away from the heart in ....
>
> and brought back in .... It supplies the tissues with ....
>
> and .... for energy, and carries ....
>
> to the lungs, where it is removed.

Q2   The pictures below show cross sections of two **blood vessels** — an artery and a vein.

a)   Which blood vessel is an artery and which a vein?

A    B

A= ....

B = ...

b)   Circle the correct word in each pair to describe how the structures of arteries and veins are related to their function.

Arteries carry blood that is at **lower / higher** pressure so have **thicker / thinner** walls than veins.

Veins carry blood at **lower / higher** pressure so a **smaller / bigger** lumen helps the blood flow

more easily. **Veins / Arteries** have valves to keep the blood flowing in the right direction.

Q3   The heart needs a constant **blood supply** to deliver the **glucose** and **oxygen** it needs.

a)   What type of cell makes up the walls of the heart?

....

b)   **i)**   What might happen if the blood supply to the heart walls is **restricted**?

....

ii)   Describe how **cholesterol** can cause a restriction in the arteries.

....

....

iii) Suggest how someone could adjust their **diet** to help control the level of cholesterol.

....

Heart Disease

Q1 Circle any of the following that do not usually **increase** the **risk** of heart disease.

microorganisms   lifestyle factors   genetic factors

Q2 Each of the factors below **increases** the **risk** of heart disease. Tick the correct boxes to show whether each of the factors is a **lifestyle** factor or a **non-lifestyle** factor.

		Lifestyle	Non-lifestyle
a)	Poor diet	☐	☐
b)	Excessive alcohol intake	☐	☐
c)	Family history of heart disease	☐	☐
d)	Smoking	☐	☐
e)	Stress	☐	☐

Q3 State two reasons why **regular moderate exercise** reduces your risk of heart disease.

1. ....

....

2. ....

....

Q4 Tick the correct boxes to show whether these statements are **true** or **false**.

		True	False
a)	Epidemiology is the study of patterns of disease and the factors that affect the spread of disease.	☐	☐
b)	Heart disease is more common in non-industrialised countries than in industrialised countries.	☐	☐
c)	Generally people in non-industrialised countries eat less junk food and so have a lower fat diet.	☐	☐
d)	Drinking excessive amounts of alcohol can increase the risk of heart disease.	☐	☐

Q5 Barry has been told that he has a **high risk** of heart disease because he is very overweight and does little exercise. However, he refuses to start an exercise programme and says "My father was even heavier than me and never did any exercise, and he lived until he was 80".

Explain what is wrong with Barry's argument.

Have a think about sample size.

....

....

Heart Disease — Correlation and Cause

Q1   Read the passage below and answer the questions that follow.

In the UK today, around 13 million adults smoke cigarettes. The consequences to health of smoking are widely accepted, especially in relation to the increased risk of lung cancer. Heart disease is as great a problem but is often overlooked as a significant risk associated with smoking.

Heart disease is a major problem in Western Europe, with 268 000 heart attacks each year in the UK alone. A recent study has estimated that 29% of all heart attacks in Western Europe are due to smoking. Tobacco smoke contains around 4000 chemicals in the form of particles and gases, some of which are thought to have harmful effects on the body.

A 50 year study (study A) showed that mortality from heart disease in Britain was 60% higher in smokers than in non-smokers. The results of this study are shown in figure 1. The study concluded that about half of all regular smokers will be killed by their habit. However the ill effects of smoking are not only felt by smokers themselves but also by those around them. Inhaling second-hand smoke can also be harmful to health. It is thought that regular exposure to second-hand smoke increases the risk of heart disease by around 25%.

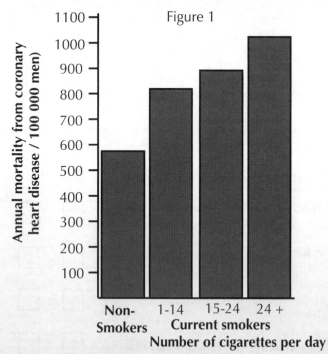

A significant proportion of the UK population are regularly exposed to second-hand smoke in the home — around 7.3 million adults and 5 million children. There is mounting evidence that this can have a serious effect on health. Many potentially toxic gases are thought to be present in higher concentrations in second-hand smoke than in the 'mainstream' smoke inhaled by smokers. These gases include ammonia and hydrogen cyanide. However, only two thirds of British adults believe that passive smoking increases the risk of heart disease.

It is becoming clear that there needs to be an increase in awareness in the risks of smoking in relation to heart disease, as well as the general long term effects of passive smoking.

Heart Disease — Correlation and Cause

a) What percentage of heart attacks in Western Europe are thought to be due to smoking? Circle the correct answer.

25%

29%

50%

60%

b) Explain why you should include as many people as possible in a study on the effects of smoking?

....

Think about reliability.

....

c) **i)** Suggest another group of people that it would have been useful to include in study A.

....

ii) Complete the passage below choosing from the words provided.

minimise	exercise	body weight	maximise	height

Studies looking at how smoking affects the risk of heart disease must try to

.... the effects of other factors. Things like the

.... of people in the study and the amount of

.... they do could also effect the risk of heart disease.

d) Does the bar chart show a **correlation** between smoking and heart disease? Explain your answer.

....

....

e) At the moment there is a ban on smoking in public buildings in some countries, but exceptions are allowed. Many people want a complete ban.

i) Suggest one reason that would be given by campaigners for a complete ban.

....

....

ii) Suggest one reason that would be given for those that oppose such a ban.

....

....

Natural and Synthetic Materials

Q1   Draw lines to match up each object with the probable source of the material used to make it.

paper bag

leather coat

car tyre

silk scarf

silkworm larva

beech tree

cows

rubber tree

Q2   Complete the statements below by choosing from the following words:

Each word can only be used once.

two   element   four   atoms   ions   mixed   bonded   material   mixture

a)   All chemicals are made up of ....

b)   An .... is a chemical made up of one type of atom.

c)   Compounds are chemicals made up of .... or more

different elements .... together.

d)   A .... contains two or more individual substances that

are not chemically joined together.

Q3   Give an **advantage** of making the following items with **synthetic** materials rather than **natural** ones.

a)   Rubber seals: ....

b)   Clothes: ....

c)   Paints: ....

Q4   Tick the boxes to show whether the following statements are **true** or **false**.

		True	False
a)	One advantage of using a synthetic material is that you can control its properties during manufacture.	☐	☐
b)	It's always more expensive to use synthetic materials rather than the natural substance.	☐	☐
c)	The pigment in paint is usually a natural material.	☐	☐

Materials and Properties

Q1   Complete the statements below by circling the correct words.

a)   A **weak** / **strong** material is good at resisting a force.

b)   You can tell how strong a material is by gradually applying a force to a sample of
the material until it breaks or is **temporarily** / **permanently** deformed.

c)   High tensile strength is when a material can resist **pulling** / **pushing** forces.

d)   Poor compressive strength means low resistance to **pulling** / **pushing** forces.

e)   Climbing ropes need a **low** / **high** tensile strength, whereas a brick low down in a wall needs
a high **tensile** / **compressive** strength to resist the weight of the bricks above it.

Q2   Complete the table by stating whether each substance
is a **liquid** or a **solid** at room temperature (20 °C).

Substance	Water	Sulfur	Propanone	Sodium chloride
Melting point (°C)	0	115	-95	801
Boiling point (°C)	100	444	56	1413
State at room temperature				

Q3   Answer the following questions about the properties and uses of materials.

a)   Steel is stiff. Suggest why steel rods are put inside concrete posts.

....

b)   Why are diamond tips used on industrial drills?

....

Q4   Use the following densities to answer the questions below.

Gold 19.3 g/cm³	Iron 7.9 g/cm³	Concrete 2.6 g/cm³
Cork 0.25 g/cm³	Pine 0.5 g/cm³	Mahogany 0.8 g/cm³

a)   Which materials from the list will sink when placed in water? (Water density = 1.0 g/cm³)

....

b)   What will happen if a large piece of mahogany is put in a bath of water?

....

Module C2 — Material Choices

<u>Making Measurements</u>

Q1 Andrew and Mark conducted similar experiments to find out how **temperature** affects the **rate** of a reaction. They mixed 10 cm³ of sodium thiosulfate solution with 10 cm³ of hydrochloric acid solution to form a yellow precipitate of sulfur. The experiment involved timing how long it took for a black cross to 'disappear' through the resulting cloudy liquid.

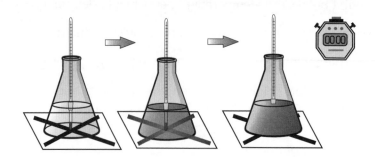

The experiment was repeated for solutions at different temperatures. Both pupils followed the same method. The tables below show their results.

Andrew

Temperature (°C)	Time (s)			
	Trial 1	Trial 2	Trial 3	Average
20	55	59	57	
30	32	31	33	
40	21	20	19	
50	13	14	13	
60	9	8	10	

Mark

Temperature (°C)	Time (s)
20	56
30	54
40	22
50	14
60	10

a) Which pupil is likely to have the more accurate results? Explain your answer.

....

....

b) Give three ways in which they could have made sure that their experiments were fair tests.

....

....

....

c) Complete Andrew's results table by working out the average time taken at each temperature.

Top Tips: It's a good idea to get some graph-drawing practice done, and also make sure that you know how to read information from graphs. It'll get you prepared for doing it trouble-free when it comes to the exam, so that you're left with plenty of time for working on the other questions.

Making Measurements

d) **i)** On the grid, plot a graph of Andrew's results. Use the average time for each temperature.

ii) Suggest why it is a good idea to use the average time from Andrew's three trials.

....

....

....

iii) Describe the correlation between temperature and time.

....

iv) What conclusion can be drawn from Andrew's results?

....

e) Compare Andrew's and Mark's results.

i) Which of Mark's results is an outlier?

....

ii) Explain your choice.

....

....

iii) Suggest two things that may have caused an error in Mark's results.

....

....

iv) At which temperature is there the greatest range in Andrew's results?

....

Materials, Properties and Uses

Q1 For each of the following questions, choose the most likely letter from the list below.

A diving suit   B milk carton   C window pane   D washing line

a) To which use would you put a low density white plastic that is hard and strong? ....

b) To which use would you put nylon fibres that are flexible with high tensile strength? ....

c) To which use would you put neoprene (waterproof, strong, but soft and flexible)? ....

d) To which use would you put polycarbonate (strong, hard and transparent)? ....

Q2 Match the following sentences with their correct endings.

Gold is suitable for jewellery because...

uPVC is suitable for guttering pipes because...

Stainless steel is suitable for knives and forks because...

Lead is suitable for paperweights because...

...it is stiff.

...it is shiny.

...it has a high density.

...it is non-toxic.

Q3 The properties of different materials make them suitable for different applications.

a) Explain why a tennis racket is made with a **metal frame** and **nylon strings**.

....

....

b) Explain why a saucepan is made with a **metal body** and **wooden handle**.

....

....

Q4 A 'mystery' material has just been discovered. It has a **high melting point**, **high tensile strength** and **low density**, and is also **flexible**, **soft**, **non-toxic** and **flame resistant**.

a) Put a ring around the product that this material would be most suitable for.

knives and forks   guttering   children's nightwear   synthetic candle wax

b) Explain how one of the properties of the 'mystery' substance make it suitable for your choice.

....

Top Tips: Some materials are great for one purpose but pretty rubbish for another. Imagine riding a jelly bicycle... In the exam, you might be asked to assess how suitable various materials are for different jobs — it's mainly common sense, but practice makes perfect...

Module C2 — Material Choices

Chemical Synthesis and Polymerisation

Q1 Tick the boxes to show whether the statements are **true** or **false**.

	True	False
a) Fossil fuels are formed from dead plants and animals.	☐	☐
b) Hydrocarbons contain carbon and water only.	☐	☐
c) Most of the crude oil we extract is used for providing energy.	☐	☐
d) Long-chain hydrocarbons are quite viscous.	☐	☐

Q2 Complete the following passage by choosing from the words below.

mixture	chains	modified	water	refines	large
	compounds	small	diesel	plastics	

Crude oil is a .... of lots of different hydrocarbons. These molecules

are .... of atoms of varying lengths. The petrochemical

industry .... crude oil to produce petrol, ... and

other fuels and lubricants. A very .... amount of the crude oil is used

to make synthetic substances — man-made .... such as

..........................., medicines and fertilisers.

Q3 For each of the following questions give the most likely answer from A - D.

a) Polymerisation is best described as ....

    A small molecules joining to form long chains   **B** large molecules joining to form long chains

    C a small number of molecules joining together   **D** two molecules joining to form one molecule

b) Polymers are usually .... based.

    A sodium   **B** sulfur   **C** carbon   **D** argon

c) Polymers are formed when small molecules are mixed under conditions of .... pressure.

    A low   **B** medium   **C** high   **D** zero

Q4 The uses of polymers depend on their properties.

a) Circle the properties that a polymer used to make window frames should have.

    flexible   strong   stiff   low melting point

b) Suggest two properties that a polymer used to make plastic bags should have.

....

Module C2 — Material Choices

Structures and Properties of Polymers

Q1   Complete the following passage by circling the correct words.

> Polymer chains are held **together** / **apart** by forces between the chains. If these
> forces are weak, the chains **cannot** / **can** slide over each other easily. This makes
> the polymer **inflexible** / **flexible** and gives it a **low** / **high** melting point. The stronger
> the bonds between the polymer chains, the **more** / **less** energy is needed to break
> them apart, and the **lower** / **higher** the melting point.

Q2   Tick the boxes to show whether the statements are **true** or **false**.

		True	False
a)	The properties of a polymer determine what it's useful for.	☐	☐
b)	The properties of a polymer depend only on the chemicals it's made from.	☐	☐
c)	A high density polymer has chains that are spread out.	☐	☐
d)	Polymers can be chemically modified to change their properties.	☐	☐

Q3   Read the following passage and then answer the questions.

In America, in the early 1830s, natural rubber was used to make various things. However, in hot weather it turned into a glue-like mess as it 'melted'. Charles Goodyear experimented by adding different substances to the rubber to try to improve its properties. By accident, he found that heating rubber with sulfur produced a hardened version of the rubber. He called the process vulcanization and set up a business making tyres.

a)   Would you describe the melting point of natural rubber as high or low?

....

b)   What is the process of hardening rubber by adding sulfur called?

....

c)   What is the cross-linking agent in this process?

....

d)   What does a cross-linking agent do?

....

....

Structures and Properties of Polymers

Q4 Polymers can be **modified** to give them different properties.

a) Give three ways in which polymers can be modified to change their properties.

1. ....

2. ....

3. ....

b) Plastics can have different chain lengths. Place ticks in the table to show the properties of short- and long-chain plastics.

	short-chain plastics	long-chain plastics
easily shaped?		
high melting point?		

c) Chemicals can be added to polymers to bond their chains together.
How does this affect the properties of the polymer?

....

....

....

Q5 **uPVC** is strong, durable and rigid. When another chemical is added to the uPVC, it becomes stretchy, soft and easier to shape. It can then be used as **synthetic leather**.

a) What is the general name given to chemicals that can be added to polymers to make them softer and more pliable?

....

b) Explain how these chemicals make the polymer softer.

....

....

Top Tips: A polymer's properties depend on how its chains are arranged and held together, as well as what chemical it is. But don't forget that polymers can be modified to change their properties. At some point, you'd better get modifying the contents of your brain to include all this stuff.

Life Cycle Assessments

Q1 Complete the passage using the words below. Each word can only be used once.

stage	cycle	environment	assess	laws	governments
sustainable		process	materials	protect	cost

The business of manufacturing things is changing as new laws are being introduced. Companies

have to .... the impact their processes and products will have on the

.... and use this information to choose a .... that does

minimal harm. It also helps them to choose the best .... for the job. They

have to look at the impact of each .... of the product's life — this is known

as a Life .... Assessment. Data from the Life Cycle Assessment enables

companies to help .... future generations.

Q2 Which stages of a product's life are being described below? Match them up.

A computer being powered by electricity.

Using the product.

Polythene being made from ethene.

Disposing of the product.

A lot of plastic bottles being thrown away.

Extracting the raw materials.

Oil being drilled out of the ground.

Manufacturing the product.

Q3 Tick the boxes to show whether the statements are **true** or **false**.

True False

a) A Life Cycle Assessment can't help in deciding the best raw materials to use.

b) The extraction of raw materials needs energy.

c) Companies always include cost as one of the factors to think about.

d) The quantity of available raw materials should be ignored in a Life Cycle Assessment.

e) Recycling materials at the disposal stage is more sustainable than putting them in landfill.

Module C2 — Material Choices

Life Cycle Assessments

Q4 Companies can use the information from a **Life Cycle Assessment** to set up manufacturing processes which have minimal environmental impact. This is a key part of sustainable economic development.

Suggest how a paper manufacturing company could become more sustainable in terms of its resources.

In short, paper is manufactured by turning wood into a mixture called a 'pulp'. This can then be rolled out into sheets of paper of any size or thickness.

....

....

....

Q5 The length of a product's life cycle can vary quite a bit.

a) Both **drink bottles** and **garden chairs** can be made from plastic (using crude oil as the main raw material).

   i) Which product is likely to have a longer useful 'life'?

     ....

   ii) Which product is likely to cost more to manufacture?

     ....

   iii) Which product is more likely to be recycled rather than being put into landfill?

     ....

Q6 A company carries out a Life Cycle Assessment for a potential new product. They discover that their planned manufacturing process would have very high environmental costs.

What could the company try to do to reduce the environmental costs of manufacturing the product?

....

....

Q7 Suggest three benefits a company might get from doing a Life Cycle Assessment.

1. ....

2. ....

3. ....

Top Tips: Life Cycle Assessments do just what you'd expect them to do — they look at each stage of the life cycle of a potential product to assess the impact it would have on the environment. Get that sorted and that'll be one less assessment you need to worry about...

Electromagnetic Radiation

Q1 Which statement best describes what we mean by **radiation**? Circle the correct letter.

    A   An invisible substance that causes cancer

    B   Something that travels as photon atoms

    C   The transfer of energy from a source

    D   The waste products of a nuclear bomb

Q2 There are seven types of electromagnetic radiation which make up a continuous **spectrum**.

a) Complete the electromagnetic spectrum below.

			visible light			gamma rays

b) Electromagnetic radiation transfers energy as **photons**.

    i) What is a photon? ....

    ii) What's the difference between a **microwave** photon and a **gamma ray** photon?

    ....

c) Which has higher energy photons? (Circle the correct option in each case.)

    i)   microwaves   ultraviolet

    ii)   violet light   red light

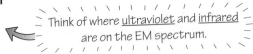

Think of where <u>ultraviolet</u> and <u>infrared</u> are on the EM spectrum.

Q3 The Sun emits EM radiation of all types. The graph shows how the **brightness** of radiation from the Sun varies with the **energy** of the photons.

a) What is the energy of the photons of the brightest radiation?

    .... J

b) From the graph, what appears to be the maximum energy of the photons that the Sun normally produces?

    .... J

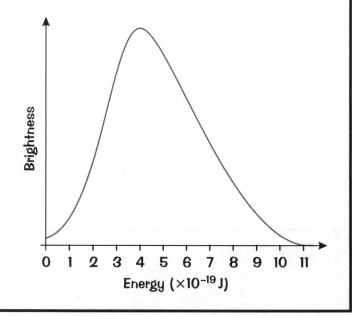

EM Radiation and Energy

Q1   Match up the terms and their definitions below. You won't need to use all the definitions.

source

reflection

transmission

absorption

detector

radiation passes through an object or a vacuum

radiation is 'stopped' by the object and the energy is deposited

an object that allows radiation to pass through it

radiation 'bounces' off an object

an object that absorbs and registers radiation

an object that emits radiation

Q2   We can **see things** because our eyes can absorb and detect the **light energy** carried by photons.

a)   Fill in the blanks to complete the sentence below:

The total energy produced by a radiation source depends on the ....
of the photons and the .... of photons it emits.

b)   100 000 photons are detected by Sarah's eye.
How much energy do these photons deliver if each photon has an energy of **0.02 J**?

....

Q3   The photons in **blue** light have **more energy** than the photons in **red** light. If a red laser and a blue laser produce the same number of photons, which delivers **more energy**? Explain your answer.

....

Q4   The brightness of a beam of light depends on its **intensity**.

a)   Explain what's meant by the **intensity** of electromagnetic radiation, in terms of energy.

....

b)   Two identically sized planets, Yurg and Zorg, both orbit the same star, as shown in the diagram.

   i)   Circle the correct words or phrases to complete the
explanation below of why **Yurg** is **hotter** than Zorg.

Yurg gets **more intense / faster** radiation than Zorg because
more photons / higher-energy photons reach Yurg every second.

   ii)   The planet Ug also orbits the same star. Ug is bigger than the other planets but **further away** from the star. Describe how the intensity of radiation on Ug will compare to that on Zorg.

....

Ionisation

Q1   Some types of electromagnetic radiation can be dangerous because they are **ionising**.

a)   Describe what ionising radiation can do to an atom.

....

b)   List the three types of electromagnetic radiation that are ionising.

....

Q2   The diagram shows a molecule being ionised. Label the **photon**, the **molecule** and the **ions**.

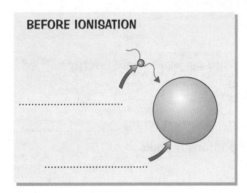

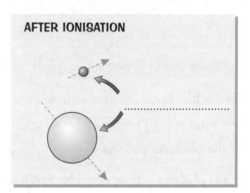

Q3   Circle the correct words to complete this paragraph about the effects of ionising radiation.

Ionising radiation can be dangerous if it forms **molecules / ions** in your cells.

It can cause **mutations / aberrations** in your **chloroplasts / DNA molecules**.

If this happens, the affected cell could start to **ionise / divide** uncontrollably —

this is **cancer / radiation sickness**. Very high doses of radiation can cause

diabetes / radiation sickness, because some of your cells **stop dividing / die**.

Q4   The Sun emits radiation in all parts of the EM spectrum, including **ultraviolet (UV)**.

a)   Explain how the Earth's **atmosphere** gives us some protection from the Sun's UV radiation.

....

b)   Describe three measures you can take to protect yourself from UV radiation.

1. ....

2. ....

3. ....

Some Uses of EM Radiation

Q1 The devices below all use EM radiation to send information.
Write down which **type** of EM radiation each one uses.

a) artificial satellite ....

b) TV transmitter ....

c) mobile phone ....

d) TV remote control ....

e) radio transmitter ....

f) 'remote central locking' car key ....

Q2 Conventional and microwave ovens both use EM radiation.

a) What type of EM radiation does a conventional oven use to cook food?

....

b) Emma bakes a potato in her microwave oven.
Describe how the microwaves affect the water molecules in the potato.

....

c) As an experiment, Emma puts an empty plastic cup in her microwave and turns
it on full for 20 seconds. Explain why the plastic cup doesn't get any hotter.

....

....

....

Q3 Write down two features of microwave ovens that prevent microwaves from **leaking** out.

1. ....

2. ....

Top Tips: A few people worry that radiation from their microwave ovens is leaking out and zapping them while they're waiting for their porridge to cook. But that's what the metal casing is for — to keep you safe (as long as you don't overheat the porridge and burn your tongue.)

Some Uses of EM Radiation

Q4 Some people worry that microwaves from **mobile phones** might be bad for their health.

a) What effect do microwaves have on living cells?

....

b) Why is using a mobile phone safer than putting your head into an operating microwave oven?

....

c) Apart from people using their phones, who else might be at risk
from the microwave radiation used by mobile phone networks?

....

....

Q5 Barry places his mobile phone **inside** his microwave oven. He then tries to phone the
mobile from his landline. Why should he be **worried** if the mobile phone rings?

....

....

....

....

*Hint — mobile phone signals
are sent using microwaves.*

Q6 A scientific report for the UK government said that there was **no evidence** that the radiation from
mobile phones was harmful, but recommended that children should limit their use of mobiles.

a) Even though there's currently no evidence of harm, why should we
still be careful about how much we use our mobile phones?

....

....

b) It's been suggested that, to reduce the risk of damage to the brain, you should send **text messages**
rather than talking on your mobile phone, and use a **hands-free set** when you do need to talk.

Explain how these measures could help.

....

....

....

*Hint — if you're talking
'normally' on a mobile,
where's the phone?*

Top Tips: Using your mobile phone is probably **not that risky** compared to, say, crossing a
busy road. But at the moment we're just **not sure** about it — mobiles haven't been used for long
enough for us to find out. Cars have been around for a while though — we know they're dangerous.

EM Radiation and Life

Q1 Electromagnetic radiation from the Sun is very important for life on Earth.

a) Fill in the gaps using some of the words in the list below.

transmitting	visible light	ultraviolet	absorbing	liquids	gases	reflecting

The Sun emits all types of electromagnetic radiation. However, various

.... in the atmosphere filter out some of this radiation by

.... or .... it. One type of

radiation that passes through the atmosphere easily is ....

b) Complete the sentence below by underlining the correct word.

The Earth's surface heats up during the day because it **reflects / absorbs / emits** EM radiation.

Q2 The equation for **photosynthesis** in green plants is: **carbon dioxide + water → sugar + oxygen**.

a) Complete the table to show which gases are added to or removed from the atmosphere during **photosynthesis** and **respiration**.

	Respiration	Photosynthesis
Gas added to atmosphere		
Gas removed from atmosphere		

b) Photosynthesis is important for humans because we get energy by **eating plants**. How else is photosynthesis important for humans?

....

....

Q3 The graph shows how the **rate of photosynthesis** in a particular plant depends on **temperature**.

a) Between which two temperatures is the rate of photosynthesis highest?

.... °C and .... °C

b) Give two reasons why the Sun is important for photosynthesis.

1. ....

2. ....

The Greenhouse Effect

Q1 The diagram below shows how the 'greenhouse effect' keeps the Earth warm.
Use the descriptions **A** to **E** to label the diagram. The first one has been done for you.

A
The Earth absorbs
radiation from the Sun.

B
The Earth emits
heat radiation.

C
Greenhouse gases
absorb radiation from Earth.

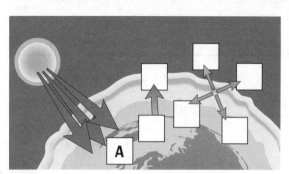

E
The greenhouse gases
emit some heat radiation
into space.

D
The greenhouse gases
emit some heat
towards Earth.

Q2 Which of the statements below is the best description
of the **greenhouse effect**? Circle A, B, C or D.

    A   Global warming caused by man's impact on the environment.

    B   A process which keeps the Earth warmer than it would otherwise be.

    C   A chemical reaction in the atmosphere which releases heat energy.

    D   The natural heating effect of the Sun.

Q3 Complete the passage by choosing from the words below.

fallen	oxygen	risen	carbon dioxide	pressures	greenhouse	temperatures

Global .... have .... in recent

years. This is due to an increased .... effect caused

by 'too much' .... in the atmosphere.

Q4 It's thought that rising temperatures will cause changes in the **climate** in many regions.

a) Suggest how climate change might affect food production.

....

b) If the Earth gets warmer, the water that makes up the oceans will **expand**.

    i) Describe how this would affect sea levels. ....

    ii) Give another reason, apart from the expansion of seawater, why sea levels would change.

....

c) Climate change may bring more **extreme weather**. Give two examples of 'extreme weather' events.

....

Module P2 — Radiation and Life

The Carbon Cycle

Q1   The diagram shows the **carbon cycle**.

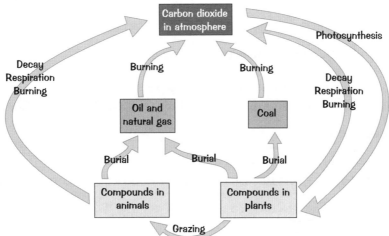

a)   Name the three processes which release carbon dioxide into the atmosphere.

....

b)   What is the only process that removes carbon dioxide from the atmosphere?

....

c)   Humans are currently cutting down and burning trees from vast areas of rainforest.
Give two reasons why this is increasing the level of carbon dioxide in the atmosphere.

1. ....

2. ....

Q2   Humans currently extract and **burn** a lot of fossil fuel, releasing carbon dioxide into the atmosphere.

a)   **i)**   Name the three fossil fuels. ....

ii) Why do we burn them? ....

b)   Complete the passage by choosing from the words below.

nuclear   plants   SO$_2$ eaten   fossil   atoms
dig up   CO$_2$ burn   decay   buried

The carbon in .... fuels comes from

.... and animals which died and

became .... a long time ago.

When we .... fossil fuels we release

this carbon into the air as ....

Module P2 — Radiation and Life

The Carbon Cycle

Q3 The carbon cycle involves living organisms as well as dead ones.

a) Complete the following sentence by underlining the correct word in each case.

All living **plants / animals / plants and animals** release carbon dioxide

into the air by **photosynthesis / respiration / decay**.

b) Bob's very proud of his compost heap — **decomposers** turn his vegetable scraps and dead plants into lovely compost which he puts on the garden each spring.

i) What are decomposers? ....

ii) Bob puts an apple core on his compost heap.
Describe how decomposers release **carbon** from Bob's apple core into the atmosphere.

....

....

....

Q4 For thousands of years the concentration of carbon dioxide in the Earth's atmosphere was approximately **constant**.

a) Circle the letter next to the best explanation for why this was.

A No carbon dioxide was added and no carbon dioxide was removed.

B Carbon dioxide was added and removed in equal quantities.

C No more carbon dioxide could be added to the atmosphere.

D The temperature was too cold for photosynthesis.

b) Over the past 200 years, the concentration of carbon dioxide has **not** been stable.

i) Describe how atmospheric CO_2 concentration has changed over this period.

....

ii) Give two reasons why this change has been occurring.

1. ....

....

2. ....

....

Top Tips: Climate change, global warming, apple cores — it's all to do with good old carbon. And you need to know all about it. And that's not just so you can pass exams — changes in the carbon cycle could have very serious consequences... which could happen in your lifetime.

Risks from EM Radiation

Q1   Read the article below and answer the questions below.

Scientists have drilled into the ice in Antarctica to obtain samples from thousands of metres below the surface. The ice at these depths was formed from snow which fell hundreds of thousands of years ago. As snow falls it traps tiny bubbles of air. Scientists can analyse the air bubbles in the ice samples to work out the carbon dioxide concentration and temperature when the ice formed. The graph shows some of this data — carbon dioxide levels in the atmosphere are rising and CO_2 levels seem to be linked to global temperature.

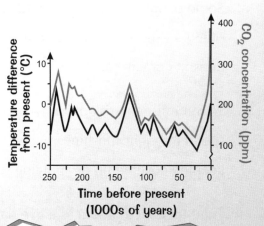

a)   Evidence shows that there is a correlation between global temperature and CO_2 concentration.

   i)   What does a **correlation** mean in this case?

   ....

   ii)   Why did scientists need to examine data for hundreds of thousands of years, rather than just a few years, to show the correlation between temperature and carbon dioxide levels?

   ....

   ....

b)   Below are five statements about climate change.
Tick the boxes to show which are **descriptions of data** and which are possible **explanations of the data**.

	Description of Data	Explanation of Data
i) Global temperatures are steadily increasing.	☐	☐
ii) Carbon dioxide levels in the atmosphere are steadily increasing.	☐	☐
iii) The rise in atmospheric carbon dioxide concentration is causing a rise in global temperatures.	☐	☐
iv) There are more extreme weather incidents every year.	☐	☐
v) Extreme weather is caused by global warming.	☐	☐

c)   Describe two measures we could take to reduce the likelihood of further global warming.

   1. ....

   2. ....

Risks from EM Radiation

Q2   Read the article below and answer the questions which follow it.

About 70 000 people in the UK develop skin cancer every year. Doctors expect this number to rise, mainly due to changes in people's lifestyles.

Some people are more likely to suffer serious damage from UV radiation than others — those with fair skin are particularly at risk. This is because fair skin doesn't contain much melanin (a brown pigment which is a natural barrier to UV).

To minimise the risk of harm, people are advised to limit the amount of time they spend in bright sunshine. When you *are* out in the sun, you can reduce the risk by keeping covered up or applying sun block.

The Met Office produces a five day 'UV index' forecast. The index is worked out by considering the position of the Sun in the sky, the expected amount of cloud cover, and the amount of ozone in the atmosphere. You can use the table below to estimate your personal risk of skin damage depending on the UV index for the day:

UV index	Fair skin (burns)	Fair skin (tans)	Brown skin	Black skin
1, 2	Low	Low	Low	Low
3, 4	Medium	Low	Low	Low
5	High	Medium	Low	Low
6	Very high	Medium	Medium	Low
7, 8, 9	Very high	High	Medium	Medium
10	Very high	High	High	Medium

a)   The population of the UK is about 60 million.

i)   What **percentage** of UK residents develop skin cancer in any one year?

    ....

ii)   Suggest one factor to do with **lifestyle** that might increase a person's risk of developing skin cancer.

    ....

    ....

Risks from EM Radiation

b) What three factors are used to work out the UV index described in the article?

1. ....

2. ....

3. ....

c) Recently, the **ozone layer** in the atmosphere over Australia has **thinned**. Explain why this increases the risk of skin cancer for people in Australia.

....

....

d) **i)** Regardless of their exposure to UV rays, some people have a higher risk of skin damage than others. What factor increases their risk?

....

ii) Explain **why** this increases the risk.

....

....

e) Barry is a roofer, so he works long hours outdoors in the summer and likes to take his shirt off. Barry's boss wants him to minimise his risk of skin cancer.

i) Suggest **two** measures Barry and his workmates could take to minimise the risk of damage to their health from UV radiation.

1. ....

2. ....

ii) Suggest how Barry's **boss** could organise the work to help reduce the risk to his workers from UV radiation.

> Hint — the Sun's radiation is most intense at midday.

....

f) Some fair-skinned people like to sunbathe for long periods of time, without sunscreen, even though they've heard that this could cause them damage. Suggest one reason why they choose to take the risk.

....

....

Evolution

Q1 Life on **Earth** is incredibly **varied**.

a) How long ago is life on Earth thought to have begun? Circle the correct answer.

350 thousand years   3500 million years   3500 billion years

b) How many species are there **estimated** to be on Earth today? Circle the correct answer.

less than 1 million   2 - 100 million   200 - 1000 million

c) Circle the correct word from each pair to complete the following sentence.

All the species on Earth today **grew** / **evolved** from very **simple** / **complex** living things.

d) Many more species have existed on Earth since life began than are around today.
What has happened to the species that no longer exist?

....

Q2 The **theory of Evolution** is generally accepted in the scientific community because there is good **evidence** to support it.

Humans and chimpanzees share lots of characteristics.

a) Chickens share 60% of their DNA with humans. How much **DNA** would you expect humans and chimpanzees to share? Circle the correct answer.

15%   55%   95%

b) Using your answer to part a), circle the correct word(s) from each pair to explain how DNA evidence supports evolution.

> **A few** / **All** species have some DNA in common, which makes sense if they have all evolved from **the same** / **different** simple life forms. The more closely related two species are, the more **similar** / **different** their DNA is.

c) How does **fossil evidence** support the theory of evolution?

....

Q3 No one knows for sure how **life** on Earth **began**.

a) One theory is that all life evolved from **simple chemicals**. What property would these chemicals need to have in order for them to develop into living species?

....

b) Suggest two places that these chemicals could have come from.

1. ....

2. ....

Natural Selection

Q1 Natural selection is all about the **survival of the fittest**.

a) Circle the correct words from each pair to complete the following paragraph.

> Living things show **valuation** / **variation**. This means some organisms are better suited to their **environment** / **species** than others. These organisms have a **better** / **worse** chance of survival. The organisms which are more likely to survive are **more** / **less** likely to breed and pass on their genes. This means **fewer** / **more** of the next generation have the favourable alleles that help them survive.

b) What does the process of natural selection cause? Circle the correct answer.

   mutation   evolution   combustion   devolution

c) Why is this good for a species?

....

Q2 Giraffes used to have **shorter necks** than they do today. Put the statements in the right order to explain how their neck length may have changed. Step two has been identified for you.

[ ] More long necked giraffes survived to breed, so more giraffes were born with long necks.

[ ] Food supplies started to become scarce.

[ ] A giraffe was born with a longer neck than normal.

[2] The giraffe had offspring who all had longer necks.

[ ] The giraffes with longer necks were able to eat more food.

Q3 Tick the boxes to show whether the following statements are **true** or **false**.

		True	False
a)	Species become better and better suited to an environment due to natural selection.	[ ]	[ ]
b)	Organisms with a better chance of survival are less likely to pass on their genes.	[ ]	[ ]

Q4 **Variation** within a species is needed for natural selection.

a) What **two** factors can cause variation?

....

b) Which of these factors can be **passed on** to future generations?

....

Natural Selection

Q5   Species evolve through natural selection to adapt to a change in their environment.

a)   Draw lines to connect the boxes to complete the following sentences.

If a species cannot evolve fast enough to adapt to an environmental change...

...then different types of organism would have been produced.

The species that exist on Earth today are the result of...

...it may become extinct.

The dinosaurs became extinct due to...

...some sort of environmental change.

If some of the events in Earth's history had been different...

...the changing conditions the planet has gone through.

b)   What might have happened to the dinosaurs if they had been able to adapt faster?

....

Q6   Put the following statements in the right order to explain how **selective breeding** is done.

☐   The process is repeated several times to develop the characteristic.

☐   Organisms with a desirable characteristic are selected.

☐   The offspring that show the characteristic best are selected and bred together.

☐   These organisms are bred together.

Q7   **Natural selection** and **selective breeding** can both change the characteristics of a species.

a)   Explain the difference between natural selection and selective breeding.

....

....

b)   Tick the boxes to show whether the changes described are due to natural selection or selective breeding.

	Natural selection	Selective breeding
i) A finch species developing sharper beaks to peck seeds more easily.	☐	☐
ii) A snail species developing stripes to camouflage with the plants in an area.	☐	☐
iii) Increasing the number of lambs born by selecting the ewes which give the most offspring.	☐	☐
iv) More dark moths found in polluted areas.	☐	☐
v) Breeding from the tomato plants that give the reddest fruit.	☐	☐

A Scientific Controversy

Q1 The statements below are observations of life on Earth. **Circle** the statements that the theory of natural selection **accounts for**, and **underline** those that **conflict** with it.

Species of finch on the Galapagos islands have different shaped beaks that suit their preferred food.

Some species' features cannot be explained by a series of smaller changes that are all advantageous.

The variety of peppered moth with dark wings became more common after the industrial revolution.

Q2 Circle the correct word(s) from each pair to complete the following paragraph.

At the time Darwin proposed his theory of natural selection, most scientists believed that all species were **changeable / unchangeable**. Darwin had the **imagination / opportunity** to see beyond this idea. Darwin's visit to the Galapagos islands gave him the **creativity / opportunity** to study species living in suitable conditions for **evolution / selective breeding**. He made careful observations and applied **creative / accepted** thinking to come up with the idea of natural selection.

Q3 Tick the boxes to show whether the following statements about evolution are based on **data** or are part of an **explanation**.

	Data	Explanation
a) Fossils from related animals have been found to be similar.	☐	☐
b) Different animals may have evolved from the same ancestor.	☐	☐
c) Natural selection is the process by which evolution takes place.	☐	☐
d) DNA from related animals shows a lot of similarity.	☐	☐

Q4 Darwin's observations conflicted with the **accepted idea** about the development of species.

a) Suggest why most scientists now accept natural selection as the **best explanation** for evolution.

....

b) Suggest a reason why some scientists still **disagree** with the theory of natural selection.

....

Top Tips: Darwin's theory of natural selection is accepted by most scientists nowadays — but it caused quite a stir when it was first published. Scientists like to argue, sorry discuss, whether new theories are any good — if they didn't, we could end up believing any old rubbish put forward.

Human Evolution

Q1   The **brain** is a very important part of the human body.

a)   How does the size of the human brain in relation to body size compare with other species?

....

b)   Suggest two ways that ancient humans were given
a survival advantage by the size of their brains?

1. ....

2. ....

Q2   The diagram below shows how **modern humans** evolved from **early man**.

a)   Circle all the species that exist **today**.

b)   What has happened to the other species?

....

c)   i)   Which of the species below would you expect modern
humans to be most similar to?
Circle the correct answer.

Homo habilis   **Homo heidelbergensis**

ii)   Give a reason for your answer.

....

....

iii) Why do all three species in part i) share some characteristics?

....

Australopithecus afarensis

Homo habilis

Homo erectus

Homo heidelbergensis

Homo neanderthalensis   Homo sapiens

Q3   In 1912, scientists discovered bones which appeared to be from an early human. However
the evidence from these bones **conflicted** with the **accepted idea** of human evolution.

a)   Give two reasons why a piece of evidence might **conflict** with an established theory.

1. ....

2. ....

b)   What effect would the discovery of **supporting** evidence have on the confidence in a theory?

....

Communication

Q1 Tick the boxes to indicate whether the following statements are **true** or **false**.

True   False

a) As multicellular organisms got bigger they became less complicated. ☐ ☐

b) Different parts of complex organisms are specialised for different jobs. ☐ ☐

c) Multicellular organisms evolved nervous and hormonal systems to coordinate and communicate between different parts of their bodies. ☐ ☐

d) The nervous system is used for slow, long-lasting responses. ☐ ☐

Q2 Complete the following passage about the nervous system by choosing the correct words.

electrical impulses   brain   stimuli   receptors   spinal cord   sense

The body has .... organs that detect ....

These organs contain ...., which send signals along nerve

cells (neurones) to the .... or .... using

....

Q3 Complete the table with the entries given to show the **sense organs** and the type of **receptors** they contain.

Organ	Receptor type
	Light
Nose	
	Sound / balance
Tongue	
	Touch / temperature

Ear

Taste

Skin

Smell

Eye

Q4 The nervous system allows you to react to a **stimulus**.

a) What are the **two** parts of the central nervous system called? Circle the correct answers.

Brain   Eyeball   Spinal cord   Liver   Sensory neurone

b) Which of the following statements best describes nervous responses? Circle the correct answer.

Fast and long-lasting   Slow and long-lasting   Fast and short-lived   Slow and short-lived

Communication

Q5 The nervous system is made up of several different parts.

a) Connect the boxes to match the following parts of the nervous system with their function.

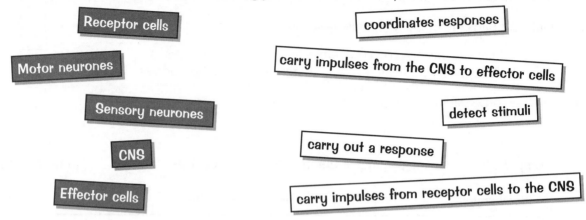

Receptor cells

Motor neurones

Sensory neurones

CNS

Effector cells

coordinates responses

carry impulses from the CNS to effector cells

detect stimuli

carry out a response

carry impulses from receptor cells to the CNS

b) Draw arrows between the boxes in the diagram to show the flow of information from a stimulus through the nervous system to the response.

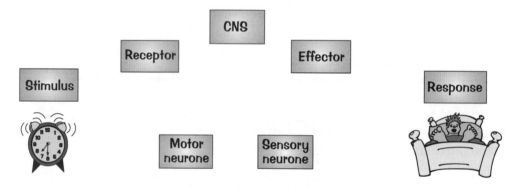

CNS

Receptor

Effector

Stimulus

Response

Motor neurone

Sensory neurone

Q6 The sensory system is driven by **stimuli**, which often trigger a **response**.

a) What is a stimulus?

....

b) **i)** What are the two types of effector in the human body?

....

ii) How does each of these effectors respond to an instruction from the CNS?

1. ....

2. ....

Top Tips: There's no need to be nervous about questions on the nervous system — just remember how all the bits work together and it'll be a piece of cake. That's a victoria sponge cake with jam and cream in the middle in case you were wondering — ooh and a nice cup of tea too.

Module B3 — Life On Earth

Communication

Q7   Complete the following passage by circling the correct word(s) from each pair.

> Hormones are **chemicals** / **impulses** which are made in **neurones** / **glands** and released into the **blood** / **brain**. They are carried around the body until they reach **a target** / **an active** cell where they act. Hormones are generally quite **fast** / **slow** to act, but their effects last a **long** / **short** time.

Q8   Tick the boxes to show whether the following responses are mainly controlled by the **nervous** or **hormonal** systems.

	Nervous system	Hormonal system
a) Hearing the alarm clock and turning it off.	☐	☐
b) Your heart beating faster when you remember you have an exam that day.	☐	☐
c) Smelling toast burning.	☐	☐
d) Your hairs standing on end when you're cold.	☐	☐

Q9   Rob is watching a horror film when some tense music starts. His **heart** starts beating more quickly and his **breathing** gets **faster**.

a)   Describe how Rob's hormonal system controlled his response to the scary film.

....

....

b)   Rob is eating popcorn while he watches the film.
Describe how his body will use insulin to help control his blood sugar levels.

....

....

Q10   Susie has been given a box of **sweets** for her birthday. She decides she would like to eat a **red** one.

Explain how her nervous system allows her to:

a)   Find the red sweet. ....

....

b)   Pick it up to eat. ....

....

<u>Interdependence</u>

Q1   The resources below are **essential** for life.

a)   Draw lines to connect the boxes to show which resources are essential for plants, essential for animals and essential for both.

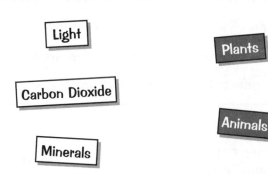
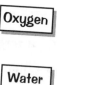

b)   What would happen if an essential resource was in short supply?

....

c)   Give one way that organisms are dependent on other species for their survival.

....

Q2   The following table shows the number of **rabbits** in a certain area over the last **five years**.

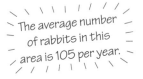

The average number of rabbits in this area is 105 per year.

Year	2001	2002	2003	2004	2005
Number of rabbits	103	128	118	109	67

a)   In which year was the number of rabbits significantly lower than average?

....

b)   Which of the following things could have **decreased** rabbit population in this year? Circle the correct answers.

Decrease in food   Decrease in predator numbers

Destruction of habitat   Disease

Q3   The **changes** described below can all **cause** species to become **extinct**. Complete the statements by circling the correct word(s) from each pair.

a)   **Environmental** / **Internal** change, such as the **construction** / **destruction** of the species' habitat.

b)   The **removal** / **introduction** of a species that is a competitor, disease organism or **prey** / **predator**.

c)   An organism that the species relies on becomes **more common** / **extinct**.

Module B3 — Life On Earth

Interdependence

Q4 The diagram on the right shows a **woodland food web**. Last year a chemical was spilt in the woods, and turned out to be poisonous to voles. As a result, the population of **voles** significantly **decreased**.

a) Draw lines to match the following **species** with the effect the **decrease** in vole population might have and what this could do to their **population** size.

Barn owl

More likely to be eaten by predators

Increase

Less food

Insects

Less competition for food

Decrease

There might be more than one effect on a species.

b) Suggest what might happen to the **bird population**. Give a reason for your answer.

....

....

Q5 The diagram shows part of a food web from Nebraska in the USA. The **flowerhead weevil** doesn't occur naturally in this area. It was introduced by **farmers** to eat the musk thistle which is a weed.

a) i) Why might the introduction of the flowerhead weevil **decrease** the number of platte thistles?

....

....

ii) What effect will this have on the population of **honeybees**? Give a reason for your answer.

....

....

b) If the population of musk thistles **decreases**, the platte thistle will have **less competition** for resources. What might this do the population of platte thistles?

....

Top Tips: Interdependence is just like happy families — dad relies on mum, the kids rely on mum and dad, mum relies on Auntie Nora... Families don't tend to eat each other though, so it's not quite the same — my sister looks like she wants to eat me sometimes, but I don't think she will.

Module B3 — Life On Earth

Humans and the Earth

Q1 Tick the boxes to indicate whether the following statements are **true** or **false**.

		True	False
a)	A species is said to be extinct when there are no more individuals of that species.	☐	☐
b)	A lot of extinctions have been caused by human activity.	☐	☐
c)	Sustainable development requires that some species are made extinct.	☐	☐
d)	Humans may cause extinction directly by irresponsibly managing habitats.	☐	☐

Q2 **Human activity** can contribute to the **extinction** of animals.

a) Match the following species to the human activity that led to their extinction.

Passenger pigeon

Dusky seaside sparrow

Tasmanian wolf

deforestation and hunting for food

destruction of habitat and killing to protect sheep

nesting sites were flooded or drained

b) The statements below describe human actions that could cause a species to become extinct. Complete the table to show which actions could **directly** cause an extinction and which could **indirectly** cause an extinction. The first one has been done for you.

Human Action	Direct	Indirect
Polluting an area of natural habitat		✓
Hunting for sport		
Killing wild animals to protect livestock		
Building a road through an area of habitat		
Introducing a new species to an area		

Q3 The **blue pike** from the Great Lakes in Canada and the US became **extinct** around 1970.

a) Suggest **two** human actions that caused the extinction of the blue pike.

1. ....

2. ....

b) State whether the actions given in answer to part a) would **directly** or **indirectly** lead to extinction.

1. .... 2. ....

Module B3 — Life On Earth

Humans and the Earth

Q4   Maintaining the Earth's **biodiversity** is very important.

a)   Which of the following statements is the best definition of biodiversity? Circle the correct answer.

> The number and variety of organisms made extinct in an area.

> The number and variety of organisms found in an area.

> Using the environment in a sustainable way.

> Protecting species from becoming extinct.

b)   Suggest how the Earth's biodiversity can be maintained.

....

c)   Complete the following passage by circling the correct word(s) from each pair.

> High biodiversity makes ecosystems **more / less** stable and more likely
>
> to **recover / deteriorate** if damaged. Maintaining biodiversity of plants
>
> means that we have **more / less** resources for developing new **nanobots**
>
> **/ food crops** and **medicines / plastics**. If an organism becomes **extinct /**
>
> **common**, the unique chemicals it produces will no longer be available.

Q5   **Gorillas** live in **forests** in Africa. The number of gorillas in the wild is
so low that many people worry that gorillas might become **extinct**.

State whether the human activities below will **increase** or **decrease** the population of gorillas.
Give a **reason** for each answer.

a)   Deforestation ....

....

b)   Setting up wildlife reserves ....

....

c)   Hunting gorillas for meat ....

....

d)   Making it illegal to buy or sell gorilla fur ....

....

**Top Tips:**   Extinction is not a good thing, I might even go as far as saying it stinks. It's up to
us humans to do something about it — if we go around wiping species out all over the place we'll
end up in a right mess. It wouldn't be so bad if little brothers were made extinct though, would it?

Module C3 — Food Matters

Organic and Intensive Farming

Q1 Use these words to fill in the blanks.

feeding   soil   excrete   microbes
leaves   cycling   decompose   roots

There is a continual .... of elements on Earth. In plants, elements are taken in through the .... and .... Animals take in elements by .... on plants or other animals. Elements are returned to the environment when animals .... or when animals and plants die and .... This process of decay is carried out by .... such as bacteria. The elements released by decay either enter the .... or go into the air, where they can be taken up again by other living organisms.

Q2 **Harvesting** crops removes various **elements** from the soil for good.

a) Name one important element that's lost from the soil when crops are harvested? ....

b) Does the fertility of the soil increase or decrease if this element isn't replaced? ....

c) Tick the boxes to show whether the statements are **true** or **false**.

                                                                     True False

i) Crop rotation helps to keep soils fertile.

ii) Organic farmers use artificial fertilisers to improve the fertility of soils.

iii) Human sewage can be used as a fertiliser on organic farms.

d) Organic farmers may grow '**green manure**'. Describe what this means.

....

e) How do intensive farmers replace elements lost from the soil?

....

Q3 A farmer grows a crop of maize in a field for six consecutive years. The yield of maize in each year is shown in the bar chart opposite.

a) Describe the trend shown by the data, and suggest a reason for it.

....
....

b) In one year there was a drought. Which year do you think this was? ....

c) Give one **organic** and one **intensive** method the farmer could use to improve his crop yields.

Organic: ....

Intensive: ....

Organic and Intensive Farming

Q4   **Organic** and **intensive** farming methods each have advantages and disadvantages.

a)   Give two advantages of using artificial fertilisers, compared to using organic methods.

....

....

b)   An intensive farmer is trying to decide whether to change to organic farming.
She compares the two methods for growing potatoes, using the information in the table.

Farming Method	Yield of potatoes per acre (kg)	Price paid to farmer (£ per kg)
Intensive	10 000	0.10
Organic	5000	0.25

i)   How much income per acre would each method produce?

....

....

ii)   Give one other economic factor that the farmer would have to consider when deciding which method is more profitable.

....

Q5   A company tested a new fertiliser, **Fert X**, to see whether it produced a better crop yield than their existing fertiliser, **OldFert**. A field was divided into two equal areas and cabbages were planted in both. In area A, 50 kg of Fert X was applied, and in area B, 50 kg of OldFert was applied. When the cabbages were harvested, area A had produced a **higher yield** of cabbages than area B.

a)   Name two **controlled variables** in this experiment.

....

....

b)   Suggest one reason why this experiment might not have been a fair test.

....

c)   The company decides to compare a test crop of cabbages grown using Fert X with a control crop, to check whether Fert X is actually an effective fertiliser. Describe how the conditions for growing the control crop should be different from those for the 'test' crop.

....

....

Pest Control

Q1 Tick the boxes to show whether the statements are **true** or **false**.

True False

a) Pests and diseases can greatly reduce crop yields. ☐ ☐

b) Ladybirds are pests that eat crop plants. ☐ ☐

c) Organic farmers control pests and diseases using man-made pesticides. ☐ ☐

d) Potato blight is a disease that can kill crop plants. ☐ ☐

e) Crop rotation can be used to control pests and diseases. ☐ ☐

f) Aphids are natural predators. ☐ ☐

Q2 Choose from the words below to complete the passage about organic farming.

control	narrow	resistant	natural	wide	man-made
	aphids	crop rotation	pesticides	predators	

Organic farmers can use .... biological processes to deal with pests and

diseases. For example, they can use .... to biologically

.... pests such as greenfly. .... can be used to

prevent a build-up of pests and diseases in one particular area. Varieties of plant can be grown

that are .... to pests and diseases. .... field edges

can be left uncultivated to encourage a large population of natural predators, such as larger

insects. Finally, natural .... can be used responsibly and with caution.

Q3 **Organic** farmers have to follow **national standards** set by the **UK Government**.

a) Give two rules the farmers have to meet before they can sell their crops as organic.

1. ....

2. ....

b) Meat standards on organic farms are also controlled by the Government.
Give two ways in which they are controlled.

1. ....

2. ....

Module C3 — Food Matters

Pest Control

Q4   Intensive farmers use **man-made chemicals** to destroy pests and diseases.

   a)   Give two advantages of using man-made chemical pesticides to treat crops.

....

....

   b)   How could pesticide spraying cause harm to humans who consume the crop?

....

   c)   What effect might chemical pesticides have on ecosystems in or near to the crops being sprayed?

....

....

Q5   Sameer and Philippa compare the prices of chicken in a supermarket.
An **organic** chicken costs £8.99, a **non-organic free-range** chicken costs
£6.99, while a **non-organic** chicken raised by **intensive battery farming**,
costs £3.99. All three chickens are the same size.

   a)   Suggest two reasons why there is a difference in price.

Think about animal welfare, growth promotion and feeding costs.

....

....

   b)   Suggest why Sameer decides to buy the organic chicken.

....

....

   c)   Suggest why Philippa buys the intensive battery farmed chicken.

....

....

Top Tips: I'm afraid to say that revision is one pest that you just can't get rid of. So, make
sure you know about the different pest control methods used by organic and intensive farmers, and
don't forget that organic farmers have to meet strict standards that are set by the Government.

Natural Polymers

Q1 Polymers are formed from the combination of lots of smaller molecules known as **monomers**.

Name two groups of compounds that are natural polymers.

....

Q2 Carbohydrates can be monomers or polymers.

a) Circle the elements below that are found in **carbohydrates**.

nitrogen   carbon   oxygen   sulfur   sodium   hydrogen   gold

b) What are the monomers of carbohydrates? Circle your answer.   **salts / sugars / amino acids**

c) Give two examples of complex carbohydrate polymers.

....

Q3 Add the labels '**glucose**' and '**amino acids**' to complete the diagrams.

a)

protein

....

b)

starch

....

Q4 Tick the boxes to show whether the statements are **true** or **false**.

		True	False
a)	Monomers are long-chain molecules.	☐	☐
b)	Polymers can be made by linking lots of monomers together in a chain.	☐	☐
c)	Proteins are natural polymers.	☐	☐
d)	Amino acids join together to form proteins.	☐	☐
e)	Proteins contain the elements carbon, hydrogen, oxygen and nitrogen.	☐	☐
f)	There are about 200 different amino acids.	☐	☐
g)	Amino acids are polymers.	☐	☐

Join the protein club! Amino acids only.

A.A.   A.A.   A.A.

Module C3 — Food Matters

Digestion

Q1   Circle the correct words to complete the sentences below.

a)   Food is made up of **small / big** molecules such as starch, proteins and fats.

b)   Digestion is the process of **breaking down / building up** large molecules.

c)   Small molecules that are **soluble / insoluble** can enter the blood.

d)   Glucose and amino acids enter the blood from the **small / large** intestine.

Q2   Match up the foods with the polymers they contain, and the monomers they're made up of.

bread / potatoes / muesli   starch   amino acids

meat / eggs / fish   proteins   glucose molecules

Q3   There are an enormous number of **different proteins** in the human body, yet there are only a small number of **different amino acids**.

a)   Explain how amino acids are able to form this huge variety of proteins.

....

b)   Give four parts of the body that are mainly made of proteins.

....

Q4   Use the words below to fill in the blanks in the passage.

urine	liver	blood	excreted	urea
proteins		excess	kidneys	growing

Amino acids are transported around the body in the .... They are

taken up by .... cells which need them to make ....

Any amino acids that cannot be used at once have to be .... These

.... amino acids are taken to the .... where they are

converted into .... This is taken by the blood to the ....,

from where it is passed out in the ....

96

Insulin and Diabetes

Q1 Diabetes involves a problem with a hormone called **insulin**.

a) Which organ in the human body produces the hormone insulin? ....

b) How does insulin help to control blood sugar levels?

....

c) Circle the correct words to complete the paragraph below.

> When you eat foods that contain a lot of sugar, the sugar enters your bloodstream
> **slowly** / **quickly**, making your blood sugar level **rise** / **fall** very quickly. Instead of
> lots of sugary food, dieticians recommend that we should eat more foods like
> **rice** / **chocolate**, that contain **complex carbohydrates** / **proteins** which are gradually
> broken down into **fat** / **sugar** by the body.

Q2 Choose from the words below to complete the passages about diabetes.

pancreas	diet	death	weekly	weight	sugar	enough
insulin	younger	responding	daily	high	brain	older

a) Type 1 diabetes usually develops in .... people, when the
.... stops producing .... Blood
.... levels can become so .... that they
damage the body, possibly causing coma and .... This type
of diabetes can be controlled with .... injections of insulin.

b) Type 2 diabetes usually affects .... people. It develops either
because the body stops making .... insulin or because the
body stops .... to it normally. Type 2 diabetes is controlled by
improving the ...., losing .... and exercising.

Q3 a) Give three of the symptoms of type 2 diabetes.

....

b) Why is type 2 diabetes becoming more common in young people?

....

....

Module C3 — Food Matters

Insulin and Diabetes

Q4 Thelma finishes eating a meal at 12 o'clock, and her **blood sugar** (glucose) levels are monitored for the next three hours. The results are shown on the graph.

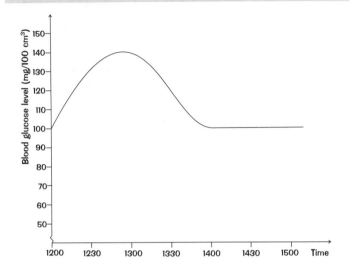

a) What is the normal blood glucose level in Thelma's blood?

....

b) By how much does Thelma's blood glucose rise after the meal?

....

c) How long does it take after finishing the meal for Thelma's blood glucose level to return to normal?

....

Q5 Nigel is a trainee doctor. As part of his training he is presented with case studies of two patients.

Patient X is 50 years old. She has visited the doctor to complain of increasing tiredness, constant thirst and a frequent need to 'visit the toilet for a wee'. On questioning, she admits to a poor diet, based on processed foods and sugar-rich soft drinks, and she is overweight. A urine test and a blood test show that she has abnormally high blood glucose levels.

Patient Y is 6 years old. She has been taken to hospital suffering from nausea and vomiting. Her symptoms have developed suddenly. She is severely dehydrated and close to falling into a coma. A blood test shows that she has abnormally high glucose levels. Patient Y's parents state that prior to this emergency, she had seemed a healthy child.

a) i) Which patient may have type 1 diabetes? ....

ii) Explain your answer. ....

....

b) What advice on **lifestyle** should the doctor give Patient X?

....

Top Tips: Normally, insulin (which lowers blood sugar levels) is produced in response to an increase in blood sugar level. Diabetics can't control their blood sugar levels properly using insulin, so it's really important for them to control their diet — to try and keep their sugar levels stable.

Harmful Chemicals in Food

Q1   Draw lines to match the foods with the dangers associated with them.

uncooked cassava

rashes, swellings, vomiting, diarrhoea and breathing problems

proteins in peanuts

cyanide poisoning

gluten in wheat

rash and swelling of the mouth and throat

Q2   In farming, both **pesticides** and **herbicides** are widely used. Pesticides are used to kill insects and other pest organisms.

a)   Why do many people try to avoid eating these chemicals?

....

....

b)   Suggest how people can limit the amount of chemical residues they get from food that's been sprayed with pesticides and herbicides.

....

Q3   Some foods can produce **aflatoxin** if they are not stored properly.

a)   Give two examples of foods which can produce aflatoxin if stored incorrectly.

....

b)   What produces the aflatoxin in these foods?

....

c)   Give one health problem that can be caused by eating food containing aflatoxin.

....

d)   Explain why it may be dangerous for humans to eat food produced for animals, such as bird seed.

....

....

Module C3 — Food Matters

Harmful Chemicals in Food

Q4 Harmful chemicals can be formed when **cooking** foods.

a) How do these chemicals cause cancer when consumed by animals?

....

b) Give three ways of reducing the amounts of these harmful chemicals in your diet.

....

....

....

c) It is known that grilling meat at high temperatures produces harmful chemicals.
Why do many people still cook meat this way? Give two reasons.

....

....

....

Q5 Potatoes produce a toxic chemical called **solanine** which is present in high
levels in the potato plant's leaves and shoots. The potato itself has a relatively
low level of **solanine**, but this level can rise if it is not stored properly. **Green**
potatoes are an indicator of high levels of solanine. Solanine concentrates
especially in the **potato skin**, and cannot be removed by washing or cooking.

For an average person, a lethal dose of solanine can be about 5 milligrams per kilogram of body
mass. Even correctly stored potatoes can contain about 200 milligrams per kilogram.

a) Calculate the lethal dose of solanine for an 80 kg person.

....

b) What mass of potatoes would need to be eaten to produce this lethal dose?

....

c) Suggest how to prepare potatoes in order to reduce the amounts of solanine eaten.

....

Top Tips: It's important to remember that just because something is eaten very commonly,
it's not necessarily completely safe. Some foods are naturally dangerous. Some contain potentially
harmful chemicals from farming. Others develop dangerous chemicals during storage or cooking.

Food Additives

Q1 Match the food additives with their descriptions.

Emulsifiers...

...thicken emulsions and help them stay mixed.

Stabilisers...

...help to stop two liquids in a food separating out.

Q2 Lots of foods contain additives.

a) Why are **food colours** added to some foods?

....

b) What is the difference between **flavourings** and **flavour enhancers**?

....

c) Why are diet drinks made with artificial sweeteners rather than sugar?

....

Q3 Choose from these words to fill in the blanks.

foul-smelling   sodium benzoate   antioxidants
oxygen   rancid   preservatives   nitrogen

Foods that contain fats or oils can go off by reacting with ....

in the air. Butter can go .... as the oxygen breaks down the

fat into .... products. To prevent this from happening,

chemicals called .... are added to food containing fats or oils.

Other foods can have ...., such as ....,

added to prevent the growth of harmful microbes.

Q4 Some food additives are thought to cause health problems.

Maths homework...
— food additives.

a) If a food additive has been given an **E number**, what does this mean?

....

b) Why might a food additive with an E number **not** be allowed to be used in the USA or Canada?

....

c) Give three health problems linked to food additives.

....

....

Keeping Food Safe

Q1   Read the information below and then answer the questions that follow.

Bovine spongiform encephalopathy (BSE) is a cattle disease that first appeared in Britain in the mid-1980s. BSE is a fatal disease of the brain. The early symptoms include disorientation and shakiness — this caused it to be popularly termed 'mad cow disease'.

A probable link between BSE and a newly discovered fatal brain disease in humans, variant Creutzfeldt-Jakob Disease (vCJD), was found, leading to an international crisis about the safety of British beef for human consumption.

This timeline shows how the problem developed:

 December 1984 — A cow on a farm in Sussex becomes the first confirmed victim of BSE, dying early in 1985. Other cows begin to show the same symptoms.

 November 1986 — BSE becomes recognised as a new cattle disease.

 October 1987 — BSE is found to be similar to the existing disease, scrapie, in sheep. Scientists begin suggesting that BSE may be caused by feeding cattle with protein derived from the carcasses of other animals, such as sheep.

 July 1988 — Many animal proteins are banned from sheep and cattle feed.

 February 1989 — An expert scientific committee, the Spongiform Encephalopathy Advisory Committee (SEAC), is established.

 November 1989 — Certain forms of bovine offal, such as brains and spleens, are banned from human foods.

 May 1990 — A pet cat is found to have a BSE-like disease. This is the first indication (outside a lab) that BSE might be able to infect a different species.

 1992/1993 — BSE reaches a peak, affecting 0.3% of Britain's cattle.

 May 1995 — The first person dies from vCJD.

 March 1996 — SEAC announces a probable link between BSE in cattle and vCJD in humans. News reports give predictions of human deaths in the UK from vCJD that range from hundreds to tens of thousands.

March 1996 — The EU (European Union) bans British beef exports.

 August 1996 — Cattle most at risk from BSE are slaughtered.

 February 2003 — Predicted deaths from vCJD are now thought to be at worst 7000.

 December 2004 — Total number of people in Britain with vCJD reaches 150.

Keeping Food Safe

a) How many years was it from BSE first appearing in cattle to the ban on using cattle brains and spleens in human food?

....

b) Explain why many animal proteins were banned from cattle feed in July 1988.

....

....

c) Give two measures that were taken to prevent the spread of BSE.

1. ....

2. ....

d) Tick the boxes to show whether the following sentences are **data** or **explanations**.

	Data	Explanation
i) In May 1990 a pet cat was found to have a disease similar to BSE.	☐	☐
ii) BSE was able to jump the species barrier and infect the pet cat.	☐	☐

e) i) Using ideas about **cost**, **risk** and **benefit**, suggest why the British Government never decided to completely ban beef for human consumption.

....

....

....

ii) What is likely to have caused the EU to ban British beef exports in 1996?

....

f) In 1992/1993 there were about 12 000 000 cattle in the UK. Approximately how many were affected by BSE?

Use data from the timeline to help you.

....

g) The first person died from vCJD relatively late into the BSE crisis. Suggest why scientists couldn't accurately predict, in 1996, how many people would die from vCJD.

....

....

Eating Healthily

Q1 Read the following newspaper article, and then answer the questions that follow.

> **'Fish Oil Supplements Boost Exam Performance'**   August 2005
>
> It has been long established in folk wisdom that a healthy body leads to a healthy mind. One school in Sheepshire has put this claim to the test by giving all its Year 11 students daily fish oil supplements in the year running up to their GCSEs.
>
> Thomasina Gradgrind, headteacher of Thwackum School, said that the improvements have been remarkable. "In 2004, 40% of our candidates achieved at least five A*-C grades at GCSE. But this year, following the use of the fish oil supplements, we have seen this boosted to 50%."
>
> There has been huge media interest in the school's project and many of the students have featured in local and national newspapers. One student, Kyle, was the subject of a documentary on national TV. "It was amazing," he said. "I used to hate school and often played truant. But this year, I settled down and studied hard for my exams. I'm really pleased with my results, and I'm hoping to begin a training course at college in September."
>
> The fish oil capsules given to the students are rich in omega-3 fatty acids, which scientists believe to be essential for brain function. These fatty acids are found in oily fish such as sardines and mackerel, but are often lacking in many people's diets.
>
> However, a leading scientist in the study of how diet affects behaviour, Professor Carlos Carlosson of Ox-fridge University, expressed doubts about the results. "I was disappointed to see that there was no proper control, and that the use of 'dummy' pills had not been included in the study. Besides, the media attention may have biased the results."
>
> Ms Gradgrind dismisses the criticism and remains convinced of the positive effects of fish oil pills. "I would like to thank all my students and staff. Everyone has made a special effort this year, and the results are terrific!"

a) i) Give one short quote from Ms Gradgrind that suggests it has not just been the fish oil pills that have caused the GCSE results to improve.

....

....

ii) A new homework club and Saturday tuition for GCSE Maths, English and Science were introduced at the same time as the fish oil pills. Why is this a flaw in the design of the experiment?

....

b) Professor Carlosson says that fish oil pills are an excellent source of omega-3 fatty acids, but it's better for people to get their omega-3 fatty acids from a **healthy, balanced diet**. Suggest why this might be the case.

....

....

Eating Healthily

c) Thwackum School has had 60 students in Year 11 in each of the previous two years. How many **more** students achieved at least 5 A*-C grades at GCSE this year than last year?

....

....

....

Look in the article to find the percentage of students achieving 5 A-C grades each year — then use these percentages to find the number of students.*

d) Professor Carlosson is concerned that the media attention may have **biased** the study. How could this attention have influenced the behaviour of Kyle, who featured in a TV documentary?

....

....

....

e) Use the information in the article and your knowledge of scientific ideas to state whether the following statements are **true**, **false**, or you **can't say**.

	True	False	Can't say
i) The GCSE results at Thwackum School improved this year.	☐	☐	☐
ii) Fish oil supplements improve exam performance.	☐	☐	☐
iii) Some students at Thwackum School took 'dummy' pills during the study.	☐	☐	☐
iv) Key Stage 3 students given fish oil supplements will get better results, on average, in their SATs.	☐	☐	☐
v) Further studies are needed for the link between fish oil supplements and exam performance to be established.	☐	☐	☐

f) Professor Carlosson conducts a new study into the influence of fish oil supplements on GCSE exam performance. He selects at random 50% of the year 11 students at Learnem School to take **fish oil supplements** for a year. The other 50% are given '**dummy**' pills. No student is told which type of pill they're being given. Their GCSE Maths results are shown in the table.

Grade		A*	A	B	C	D	E	F	G	other
No. of students	Dummy pills	3	5	10	18	16	10	5	3	0
	Fish oil pills	4	4	12	18	14	12	3	2	1

i) How many students in total were involved in this study?

....

ii) Calculate the percentage of students obtaining grades A*-C in each group.

Students taking fish oil pills: ....

....

Students taking 'dummy' pills: ....

....

Radioactivity

Q1   Label this diagram of an **atom** with the words below.

nucleus   protons   neutrons   electrons

....

(made up of ....

    and ....)

....

Q2   **Draw lines** to connect the beginning of each sentence with its ending.

Radioactive atoms are...

Unstable atoms decay...

The decay is spontaneous...

When atoms decay...

The three types of radiation are...

...they give out radiation.

...and not affected by physical conditions.

...at random and unpredictably.

...unstable and decay to become stable.

...alpha, beta and gamma.

Q3   What effect would adding a **catalyst** to a radioactive sample have on the amount of radiation given off by that sample?

....

Q4   Complete the passage by choosing from the words provided.

size	atom	protons	mass	electrons

Most of an .... is empty space. Most of the

.... of an atom is concentrated in its nucleus.

.... move around the outside of the

atom. Their paths give the atom its overall ....

Radioactivity

Q5 Underline the **factor** that can affect the amount of **radiation** emitted by a radioactive source.

The air pressure around the sample

The shape of the sample

How much of the substance there is

Q6 Complete the table below to compare the three types of radiation.

Type of radiation	What is it?	Relative size	Penetrating power	Speed
alpha	a particle		low	
beta		small		
gamma				extremely fast

Q7 Answer the following questions about **gamma radiation**.

a) Under what circumstances would a nucleus emit gamma radiation?

....

b) Why is a substance that produces gamma radiation difficult to store safely?

....

Q8 The ability of radiation to **penetrate** a material depends on what **kind** of radiation it is.

a) Which type(s) of radiation could escape from a **paper bag**?

....

b) What is the only kind of radiation that will pass through a thin sheet of **aluminium**?

....

c) Which type of radiation can only be stopped by a thick **lead sheet** or very thick **concrete**?

....

Half-Life and Background Radiation

Q1 Tick the boxes to show whether the following statements are **true** or **false**.

True False

a) The number of radioactive nuclei in a sample always stays the same. ☐ ☐

b) Different radioactive materials decay at different rates. ☐ ☐

Q2 Complete the following sentences using some of the words given below.

| short | quickly | decay | half | long | melt | slowly | all |

a) The half-life of a sample is the time taken for .... of the radioactive atoms present to ....

b) A long half-life means that the activity falls ....

c) A short half-life means that the activity falls .... because a lot of the nuclei decay in a .... time.

Q3 The half-life of strontium-90 is **29 years**.

a) If you start with 1000 atoms of strontium-90, how many will be left after 29 years?

....

b) After another 29 years, how many will be left? Circle the correct amount.

250   **0**

Dave regretted performing a DIY X-ray on himself.

Q4 Join up the beginnings and endings of the sentences below by drawing lines.

Background radiation is...

Natural radioactive materials...

Cosmic rays are...

Human activity that causes radiation...

Cosmic rays...

...come mainly from the Sun.

...a source of background radiation.

...includes nuclear explosions.

...radiation that is all around us.

...include soil, rocks and the air.

Q5 For a radioactive material to be considered **'safe'**, its emitted radiation should be at or below the normal **background level**.

a) A sample of cobalt-60 has an activity of **24 Bq**. The background count is **6 Bq**. The half-life of cobalt-60 is **5 years**. How long will it take for the sample to reach a 'safe' level of activity?

....

b) What would be the safest material to **store** the sample in until it is 'safe'?

....

Danger from Nuclear Radiation

Q1   Complete the paragraph below using the words in blue.

cells	cancer	ions	radiation sickness	kill	break	ionising

Alpha, beta and gamma radiation are described as ....
radiation because when they hit molecules they .... them
into bits called .... Ions can cause serious damage to
.... in the body. A high dose of radiation will
.... cells, causing ...., whereas
smaller doses damage cells, which can cause ....

Q2   Would you expect the following people to be at a
normal or **higher than normal** risk of radiation exposure?

a) Coal miners ....

b) Lumberjacks ....

c) X-ray technicians in hospitals ....

d) French teachers ....

Q3   We can be affected by radiation in two ways — **contamination** and **irradiation**.

a) Explain the difference between contamination or irradiation.

....

....

b) State whether the following situations are examples of **contamination** or **irradiation**:

i)   Breathing the dust from a nuclear explosion. ....

ii) Flying in a plane at high altitude. ....

iii) Picking up some radioactive material in your hand. ....

iv) Eating fish from a lake that has had radioactive material dumped in it. ....

v)   Walking through a uranium mine. ....

Top Tips: Annual radiation doses can vary a fair bit from person to person. Everyone's
exposed to a low level of **background radiation** every day, though — from rocks, etc. — and you can't
do anything about that (unless you fancy wearing a lead-lined suit and breathing apparatus all day long).

Module P3 — Radioactive Materials

Danger from Nuclear Radiation

Q4 Tick the boxes to show whether the following statements are **true** or **false**.

		True	False
a)	Radiation always kills you.	☐	☐
b)	Only some people are exposed to radiation every day.	☐	☐
c)	Airline pilots are exposed to more radiation than the average person.	☐	☐
d)	Alpha particles are always harmless.	☐	☐

Q5 **Radiation dose** is measured in sieverts (Sv).

a) Circle the letter next to the correct definition of radiation dose.

A A measure of how much radiation would be absorbed by the body.

B A measure of the ionising power of a sample of radiation.

C A measure of the possible damage done to your body.

b) Write down two factors that a radiation dose depends on.

1. .... 2. ....

c) While you are reading this, you are receiving about 2 mSv/year. What is causing this?

....

d) The table shows some typical radiation doses.

i) Suggest why living in Cornwall is more risky than living in many other places in the UK.

....

....

....

ii) Suggest why airline staff are considered to be at a higher risk of radiation exposure than most people, even though the average dose from a single flight is very low.

....

....

....

	Dose in Sv
Dose required to sterilise medical products	25 000 (single dose)
Typical total radiotherapy dose to cancer tumour	60
50% survival probability, whole body dose	4 (single dose)
Max. worker dose limit allowed by law (whole body)	0.02 per year
Average dose from all sources in Cornwall	0.008 per year
Average dose from background radiation in UK	0.002 per year
Typical chest X-ray dose	0.00002 (single dose)
Average dose from a UK to Spain flight	0.00001 (single dose)

Uses and Risks of Nuclear Radiation

Q1   Gamma radiation can cause cancer. It's also used to treat cancer by **radiotherapy**.

a)   Explain why radiotherapists use a **narrow** beam of gamma rays, and **focus** it carefully onto the cancer cells.

....

b)   Why do patients often feel very ill after radiotherapy?

....

Q2   Irradiation with **gamma rays** is widely used in the USA to **sterilise food**, but in the EU this is mainly restricted to spices. The food is packaged and then passed through a beam of gamma rays.

a)   What is the **advantage** to a shopkeeper if the food they stock is irradiated?

....

b)   Tick the boxes to show whether the following statements are **true** or **false**.   **True   False**

i)   Gamma rays are used because they are more ionising than alpha or beta radiation. ☐   ☐

ii)   Gamma, beta and alpha radiation could all pass through foil packaging. ☐   ☐

iii)   The food will not be radioactive after irradiation. ☐   ☐

Q3   **Surgical instruments** used to be made of metal and were sterilised by **boiling**. Now, many are made of plastics.

a)   What does 'sterilise' mean?

....

b)   Why can't plastics be sterilised by boiling?

....

c)   Instruments are often sterilised **after** they have been sealed in plastic bags. Why is sterilisation of the instruments still possible?

....

d)   The gamma source used to irradiate instruments normally has a long half-life. Why is this?

....

Module P3 — Radioactive Materials

Uses and Risks of Nuclear Radiation

Q4 It's likely that new **nuclear power stations** will be built around the UK in the near future as a way of reducing the **carbon dioxide** emissions that are produced when fossil fuels are burned. These will bring **benefits** to many people but some people see them as very **risky**.

a) For each of these groups of people explain the **benefits** of building a new nuclear power station.

i) construction companies

....

ii) local people *Remember power stations are often built in remote areas of the country.*

....

iii) the whole country's population

....

b) For these groups suggest the **risks** they might be concerned about.

i) local people

....

ii) the whole country's population

....

Q5 Radioactive isotopes can be used as **tracers** in medicine. One example is **technetium-99**, which is injected into a patient to investigate **kidney blockages**. It has a **short half-life** (about six hours) and only gives off **gamma radiation**. By using a **radiation detector**, doctors can track the movement of the tracer and can tell whether it **leaves** the kidneys when it should.

a) What is the **risk** of injecting a radioactive material into the body?

....

b) What is the **benefit** of injecting a radioactive material into the body?

....

c) Why is it important that a radioactive source used in this way has a **short half-life**?

....

d) Why is a **gamma** source used rather than an **alpha** source?

....

Electricity

Q1   Electricity is a **secondary** energy source. Coal is a **primary** energy source.

   a)   What does the word 'secondary' mean in this context?

....

   b)   How is electricity **transmitted** from its source to the rest of the country?

....

   c)   Why is electricity a very **convenient** energy source?

....

Q2   Choose from the words below to complete the main steps
in the production of electricity in a gas fired power station.

| potential   turbine   generator   motor   steam   burned   kinetic |

Gas is .... to release energy. ➡ The energy is used to

produce .... from water. ➡ The steam is used to turn a

.... ➡ The movement (..................................... energy)

is converted into electricity by a ....

Q3   Generating electricity from **coal** is not very **efficient**.

   a)   How is energy **released** from the coal? ....

   b)   Give two ways in which energy is **wasted** inside a coal-fired power station.

1. ....   2. ....

Q4   Below is a **Sankey diagram** for the generator and
distribution of electricity from a **gas fired** power station.

1000 J input
energy from
gas

600 J useful
electrical energy
in the home

322 J   50 J   28 J heat
heat   noise   in wire

   a)   Explain what the thickness of the arrows tells you.

....

....

   b)   Calculate the efficiency of the process shown in the Sankey diagram.

....

   c)   In what form is the most energy lost? ....

Module P3 — Radioactive Materials

Generating Electricity — Non-Renewables

Q1 **Fossil fuels** (like coal) and **nuclear fuels** (like uranium) are **non-renewable** resources.

a) What does 'non-renewable' mean?

....

b) Apart from coal and uranium, name two other non-renewable fuels.

....

Q2 Which of these statements are **true** and which are **false**?

		True	False
a)	All non-renewable fuels produce carbon dioxide when they are used.	☐	☐
b)	Burning coal produces carbon dioxide.	☐	☐
c)	Carbon dioxide contributes to the 'hole' in the ozone layer.	☐	☐
d)	Nuclear power is not responsible for carbon dioxide emissions.	☐	☐
e)	Global warming is partly caused by burning coal.	☐	☐

Q3 Fill in the missing words in the paragraph by choosing words from the list. You may need to use some words more than once.

| electricity | mined | power stations | nuclei | carbon dioxide | energy | uranium |

In a nuclear power station the fuel used is .... Large amounts of

.... are released from the fuel when its ....

split. This process doesn't release any .... into the atmosphere,

although some is produced when the uranium is ....

Q4 **Nuclear power stations** produce **radioactive waste** that is difficult to dispose of. Some people think this makes nuclear power an **unsustainable** technology. Circle the correct word in each of the following sentences.

a) Clothing that has been used by nuclear technicians is an example of **low / intermediate / high** level waste.

b) A lot of heat is generated by **low / intermediate / high** level waste.

c) The casing of fuel rods is an example of **low / intermediate / high** level waste.

d) **Low / Intermediate / High** level waste is sealed into concrete blocks and put into steel cans.

e) **Low / Intermediate / High** level waste is sealed into glass and steel and allowed to cool for 50 years before permanent storage.

f) **Low / Intermediate / High** level waste is buried in secure landfill sites.

Generating Electricity — Renewables

Q1 The Government has a target to produce **10%** of our electricity from **renewable** resources by **2010**.

a) What do we mean by renewable resources?

....

b) Name two renewable resources used to generate electricity.

....

c) Why do renewable resources normally **damage** the environment **less** than fossil fuels?

....

Q2 a) Circle the **renewable resources** from the list below.

solar

wind

biomass   natural gas   geothermal

b) Name two renewable resources that can only be used in **some places**, and briefly explain why.

Resource: ....

Reason: ....

Resource: ....

Reason: ....

Q3 Underline any statements that are correct.

Solar cells produce electricity using the heat from the Sun.

Solar cells only work in hot countries.

Solar cells are useful for appliances that don't need much energy.

Solar cells use materials like silicon to convert light energy into electricity.

Solar cells have no fuel costs and don't produce carbon dioxide.

Q4 Use the words below to complete the passage about wind power.

coast	wind	hill	generators	turbines	windy	blades	carbon dioxide	offshore

Wind turbines have .... inside them which produce electricity when the .... turns the .... of the turbine. Wind turbines can only be used where it is .... most of the time, such as on a ..../ near the .... or .... There are no fuel costs because .... is free. The other advantage is that no .... is produced.

Module P3 — Radioactive Materials

Electricity in the Future

Q1   Read the passage below and answer the questions that follow.

Is Nuclear the Way to Go?

Our world relies on electricity as a convenient way to run almost every household and business appliance you could think of — from hairdriers to personal computers.

Current methods of generating electricity rely heavily on burning fossil fuels. But this is not sustainable for two reasons. Firstly, the supply of these fuels is limited and rapidly diminishing. Secondly, the carbon dioxide released when fossil fuels are burnt is having a major effect on the Earth's climate.

The two options, if we want to go on using electricity as we currently do, are to use renewable energy sources, such as wind power, or to use nuclear power.

The Government is seriously thinking of building more new nuclear power stations, in a bid to reduce the country's carbon dioxide emissions. At the same time several large-scale wind farms are being proposed at various sites around the UK.

There have been several public enquiries into the siting of wind farms and the arguments have revolved around the potential benefits of wind energy versus the environmental drawbacks.

Those in favour of the wind farms have argued that being able to produce electricity sustainably, and not generating carbon dioxide, far outweighs any environmental harm they might do.

Those against the proposals have argued that the wind turbines would cause visual pollution — they are usually to be sited in the most beautiful areas of the country, such as the Lake District. They also have concerns about the effect on migrating birds and the noise pollution caused by the rotating blades.

New nuclear power stations have not yet reached the public enquiry stage. When they do, the arguments are likely to be about the benefits of producing electricity without carbon dioxide emissions, against the safety concerns of the local population and the problem of waste disposal. Another factor is the time it will take to build the nuclear power stations compared to the time needed to set up wind farms.

	Wind	Nuclear
CO_2 emissions per unit of electricity produced (g)	0	110 (due to uranium mining, transport and processing)
Build time (including planning consent)	3-4 years	10-15 years
Lifetime of site (years)	25	25
Cost of each unit of electricity produced	3-4p	4-7p
Decommissioning cost of one turbine	Relatively low	Very high
Typical output of power station / wind farm	60 MW (enough for 40 000 homes)	1200 MW (enough for 800 000 homes)

Electricity in the Future

a) Give two reasons why we'll need to **change** the way we **generate electricity** in the future.

1. ....

2. ....

b) **i)** Calculate the amount of carbon dioxide produced in generating 3 units of electricity using nuclear power.

....

ii) Calculate the carbon dioxide emissions produced in generating 3 units using wind turbines.

....

c) Underline any arguments, from those below, that could be used **against wind power**.

Wind energy can only be used when the wind blows.

It is expensive to produce electricity from wind power.

Wind turbines are often seen as visually unattractive.

d) Assuming nuclear power stations can be operated safely, what is the biggest **long-term** problem associated with nuclear power?

....

e) Why is the energy output of a wind farm less reliable than that of a nuclear power station?

....

f) If demand for electricity was **rising sharply**, would it be more sensible to start building wind farms or nuclear power stations? Explain your answer.

....

....

g) Suggest why the **build time** of a wind farm is much less than that of a nuclear power station.

....

....